STAINES MDF The B
SELF HELP GROUP

GW00361017

Overcoming Depression

and

Manic Depression
(Bipolar Disorder)

A
Whole-Person
Approach

by Paul A. Wider, M.A.

Published by: *Wellness Communications*

Warning: Depression and Manic Depression (Bipolar Disorder) are very serious conditions. People who suffer from these ailments should be under the care of a doctor and in therapy. The intention of this book is to be an adjunct to and not a substitute for these. All concerns and any changes in treatment of these conditions related to your health care require medical supervision.

Published by:
Wellness Communications
120 Morse Ave.
Rutherford, NJ 07070-1128

Library of Congress Control Number: 2001089261

ISBN 0-9649151-7-0

Ordering information may be found at the end of this book

To solicit the author for a seminar at your location,
or to offer feedback:
Write *Wellness Communications* at the above address,
call us at 201-804-7735,
or visit the following web site:

www.manicdepression.org
The author's email address may be found here.

Printed in the U.S.A.
by Morris Publishing, Kearney, NE 1-800-650-7888

Warning!

The book you are reading uses a multifaceted approach to moderate the symptoms of depression and manic depression (also termed bipolar disorder or bipolar depression). Having had this disease (dis-ease) myself, and having also dealt with immediate family members who suffer from the same disease, I do not take this matter lightly.

I understand first hand that the person who is directly afflicted with this disease suffers immensely, for I, myself have suffered in this way. I also know the powerless feeling and great anguish of those who are close to a person experiencing such huge mood swings. I have been in that position, as well.

People have differing opinions on the use of medication. Many people use ongoing medication in order to stabilize their moods while under the care of a psychiatrist. This is the approach recommended by most psychiatrists. There are others who choose not to use medication and seek mood stability through other means. Such people may not believe in medication, may be concerned with side-effects of medications, or may have tried medications which have not worked for them. Still others may take medication when their symptoms are severe. Then after they have been stable for some time, with the supervision of their psychiatrist, they wean off the medication. This should only be done after receiving some good therapy and putting several other support systems in place. The need, or lack of need, for medication is very individual and depends upon the severity of the symptoms. Keep in mind that most mental health professionals would agree that **Counseling is necessary with or without medication.** Whatever your present state—know that you can get better. You can improve!

> **I do not encourage anyone to stop taking medication,** especially if it has saved his or her life, or brought him or her back from chaos (harm of self and/or others) to a healthy level of functioning. The responsibility for taking or not taking medication lies <u>solely</u> in the hands of each individual who is faced with that decision, or their family if the individual is incapacitated or under-age. That decision should be made under the supervision of the person's doctor or psychiatrist.

*The methods in this book can be very beneficial to a person who chooses to take medication as well as to someone who prefers a non-drug approach. **Medication alone is usually not a cure-all! There are many other issues that generally fuel depression and bipolar disorder.** This book* *will help the reader understand these issues and offer ways of healing them for the medication-user or non-medication-user as well.* The wholesome methods in this book have been wrought through pain and suffering, hard work, much research on the subject and a great determination to get well and stay well.

For the person who chooses not to take medication the following guidelines are imperative:

1.   They must first admit that they have a problem——that they have something which needs to be healed. In short, the person must *take responsibility* for their disease. If a person is in denial and won't admit that they have a problem, a non-drug approach will probably not be effective for them. It may even be dangerous to try!

2.   The person who suffers from *bipolar disorder* needs to acknowledge that they have swings on "both" sides, an *up-side* as well as a *down* side. An **awareness** of their *above average* mood swings (highs and lows) is necessary for healing. In addition, the person must be willing to change. Specifically, he or she must actively take steps to moderate the highs as well as the lows. If a person will not let go of the highs (or lows), healing will be most difficult, or even impossible.

3.   If the person's cycles are too extreme, or if he or she is far out of touch with reality, it will be hard or impossible to begin with a non-drug approach. The use of medication will probably be necessary until their mood is stabilized for a time.

4.   The person needs to be willing to work at a program to deal with their disease. He or she must be determined to get well, and stubborn about doing what it takes to get well and stay well.

5.   The person must set up a support network. It is imperative to have strong support, since the drug-free road to attain mood stability is not easy. Remember, we can do together what we cannot do alone. Support should consist of a Psychiatrist, a therapist and a support group. Twelve step support groups such as Codependents Anonymous (CODA), Adult Children of Alcoholics (ACOA), or Al-Anon work well for many people. Twelve step groups address numerous issues that can be helpful to people who suffer from depression or bipolar depression.

6.   The person's stress levels must be low. High stress is one of the major triggers of bipolar depression. If a person is living in an extremely stressful situation or experiencing high levels of stress from within, those stresses *must* be relieved before using a non-medication approach.

7.   Hopefully, the person's family will support the person in whatever method he or she *chooses* to heal, and not try to force the person to do it *their* way. My parents did not support me in my choice and that caused me great pain. If family is not supportive of the approach you choose, or worse, if they are vehemently against your approach—you must find friends and/or a substitute family who do support you, encourage you and believe in you.

8.   Hopefully, the person's psychiatrist also will be supportive of the person's choice. *Most medications that are stopped should not be stopped abruptly, but rather tapered off gradually, since there may be a withdrawal reaction upon rapid cessation of medication. A withdrawal reaction could trigger another depression or bipolar episode.* Information on medication—concerning how to take it, what it's side-effects are and how to stop taking it can be found by asking your doctor or local pharmacist. There is another resource for learning about medications, including the negative side-effects they can cause, and how to stop taking psychiatric medications. It is psychiatrist Peter Breggin's book: *Your Drug May Be Your Problem: How and Why to Stop Taking Psychiatric Medications (See Appendix B). If you choose to change or stop medication, I recommend you do it with a psychiatrist's supervision.* There are psychiatrists who will support you if you look hard enough.

        If, after working with a psychiatrist or doctor to taper off medication, you should fall into a severe depression or high, you can quickly resume taking medication again. If you do not work with a doctor and you relapse after tapering off medication, it will take much longer to get back on medication and become stabilized again. Work closely with a psychiatrist. Discuss carefully with him or her the benefits, side-effects, risks of taking medications, risks of   not taking medication and alternative treatment options.

THANK YOU

Without my friends, without my family, without God, I would not be here, and I would not be healed. The people who have helped me along my journey are too numerous to mention. I would, however, like to acknowledge the following persons and the ways they have helped me return to wholeness. (Please note words in *italics*, for they have been very powerful in my healing.)

First, I would like to thank *God*, who is behind everything and in everyone. Thank you, Lord, for your words are true: "Come to me all you who are burdened and I will give you rest."

Next, I would like to thank you, Mom—and my Dad who has passed on. It is you who have given me the gift of life. I know that you have nurtured me to the best of your ability. I also know that each of you went through your own personal hell. I realize you have sacrificed much for me, and for that I am grateful. Please know that I have worked through my pain and anger to a point of forgiveness and love. I love you both.

Thank you, my sister Cathy. It is the great love I have for you that has provided much motivation for this book. Thanks for your *encouragement*, Cath.

Thank you Juan Pena, my friend, for reaching down into the pit I was in and helping me get out. I will never forget the countless days you sat and talked with me, and encouraged me, but most of all *you believed in me*. I still remember when you said, "Never give up buddy, never give up, never give up, never give up!"

Thank you, Wayne Kretzing, my friend. You have stuck by me through thick and thin. *You patiently listened to me* when I was flying high and talking a mile a minute. You took me for hikes when I was so depressed and didn't even want to leave the house. Thank you for not leaving me. *You have provided consistency and love in my life.*

Tom Tuite, my friend, *when you listened to me, I didn't feel judged. I felt your compassion.* You were a person of few words. But when you did speak, your carefully chosen words were pointed like an arrow at my heart, to build me up. I sensed *you believed in me*.

Tina, thank you for loving me, even to the point of great personal cost. Thank you for instinctively holding me in your arms and cradling me when I was depressed. That *broke the spell* and allowed me to weep and release my grief when I was depressed. I could not do that before.

Bob McParland, thank you for being my friend. Thank you for *accepting me as I am and encouraging me* with your words and by your example (to follow my dream, leaving money, security, and benefits behind). *Thank you for your charitable and committed effort in editing this book.*

Thank you Judy, my therapist. You were the turning point in my struggles. Just to summarize what you gave me would take a page to tell. That page is dedicated to you later in this book.

Reuben Henriquez, thank you for your kind offer and follow through in drawing the illustrations for this book. Your charity is inspiring and the characters you drew fit this book so well.

Elliot Udenfriend and Maaike Callan, thank you for believing that my book should get out to people to help them. Thank you for the many charitable hours you put into editing this book.

Thank you, Diana Fitter, for your charitable and kind effort in finishing the cover of my book with your professional touch.

Thank you Barbara Palumbo for your charitable and professional addition of an index to this book. Thank you also for creating an electronic version of this book and your final professional editing touches.

Thank you, Dawn, my wife, for *believing in me* and *encouraging me* to pursue my dream. Thank you for all of your work in editing several revisions of this book. Thank you for the *good consistent and determined love* you give me. Thank you for *accepting and loving all of me.* You have brought new hope and energy to my dreams. I love you, Dawn.

Thank you Ann Mancuso, Nick Zwetkow, Paul Fitter, Sheila Hyun, Jill Amato, Walter Smith, my friends at CODA, My friends at MDSG, Joan Marie, Gerry Gilmore, Evelyn DeSent and all those I haven't mentioned— you know who you are. Thank you all!

ACKNOWLEDGMENTS

Excerpts from *The Road Less Traveled* copyright © 1978 by M. Scott Peck, M.D. Reprinted with permission of Simon & Schuster, Inc.

Excerpts from *The Secret of Staying in Love* by John Powell, S.J. © 1974 John Powell, S.J. Tabor Publishing, Allen, Texas 75002. Reprinted by permission of RCL Enterprises Inc. Representative of Tabor Publishing.

Excerpts from *The Low Blood Sugar Handbook* by Edward and Patricia Krimmel, © 1992 Franklin Publishers, PO Box 1338, Bryn Mawr, PA 19010. Permission was granted by Edward and Patricia Krimmel.

Excerpts from *American Journal of Psychiatry*. Article titled: *Life Events and the Course of Bipolar Disorder*. Permission granted by the Dr. Constance Hammen, UCLA.

Scripture taken from the Holy Bible, New International Version. Copyright © 1973, 1978, 1984 International Bible Society. Used by permission of Zondervan Bible Publishers.

CONTENTS

Chapter 1

HOPE

A re you feeling depressed? Do you suffer from bipolar disorder—once called manic depression or bipolar depression? If so, take heart. I know it is a terrible way to feel, so I will not make light of it. However, there is hope! There *is* light at the end of the tunnel. Recovery from this darkness is possible. I assure you, for I am experiencing it now, after living with and working through my own bipolar depression. For over a decade, I am in recovery and am in control, rather than an illness or disease controlling me. I prefer to call it a dis-ease. I also have family members who have struggled with the same disease. I have experienced both sides: what it is like to suffer from the disease itself and what it is like having family members who have the problem.

So why say, "take heart"? Without the rain, can there be a rainbow? Without the night, can we appreciate the dawn?

Did you know that many great people have struggled with depression or bipolar? Abraham Lincoln, Albert Einstein, Theodore Roosevelt, Winston Churchill, Ernest Hemingway and Saint Francis of Assisi are a few of these. Are you a great person? Yes, you are. We all are. It's often just a matter of breaking through the surface stuff, to get through to the greatness that is in us all. We must get to the real person. We must get to the person behind the mask which many of us wear, the person that is *who we are*, the unique person who has a special place in the Master's plan which only he or she can fill, the person who has a *reason to live*, a *purpose in life*.

My wish is to offer you hope and the incentive to find the solution to your own problem, whatever it may be. For, surely, an answer does exist!

It is from where I have been, compared to where I am now, along with a deep love for my fellow brothers and sisters in the human family—especially those who are suffering—that I wish to share my story and the things I have learned on the journey to wholeness. My hope is that the *tools* contained in this book which have been gathered from many sources might be used to facilitate healing for those who are on a similar journey and in a painful place. As the tool makers left us the wedge, the lever and the wheel, I leave you with thoughts and encouragement to make life's journey much more enjoyable. Most of all, I offer my love. For love is the reason that we are here: love of God, love of self, and love of others; *love*, that's all. Though, when one understands what love really is, that's a lot.

My depressions have helped me to break through some of the surface stuff. I picture it as being like an onion. Imagine that a diamond is at the core of an onion. Many layers must be removed before you are able to get to the core. These can be peeled off, or one may use a knife to cut to the heart of the onion. I believe that depression is the knife. It helps one to cut through the layers of ignorance and get to the diamond at the core.

It has been said that many of the greatest contributions to humankind have been accomplished by those who have suffered immensely. From this, I have learned that a person who suffers much is very special. I wondered, "Could it be that I would some day accomplish something great?" Maybe I would have a strong positive impact on others because I had endured the cross of my depressions. Could it be turned around? This thought increased my hope. Wonderful, since *hope is the opposite of hopelessness* and hopelessness is a major factor in causing and perpetuating depression.

As for my story: in the past, I have experienced times of severe depression. I have been depressed for several months at a time. Compounding the depression was the awful feeling of paranoia. I felt that people were out to get me, that people were trying to kill me at times—or at least that people would like to see me dead. I, in fact, wished I was dead. I thought of many ways to do myself in. Some types of fear are usually not good, but it was fear that kept me from killing myself. Fear that the other side might be worse. That even though this—what I was going through—seemed like hell, I thought *real hell* would be even worse. So I was afraid to kill myself. Thank God for this kind of fear. I am now very glad to be alive.

16

When I was depressed for months at a time, I quit my job and just sat around the house doing nothing but worrying. At a certain point, I realized that this was not good and tried to do some things to occupy my mind. I watched TV for hours and hours. I cleaned the house or washed windows. Although I felt hopeless and that there was no way out of the way I was feeling, these simple activities helped a bit. They gave me at least a little feeling of worth and accomplishment. I also read a bit, and grace led me to find a book called *Psychosomatics* (listed in Appendix B), which I read. This book increased my hope as it pointed out a connection between *what we think* and *the illnesses that we suffer from.*

When I was depressed, I slept a lot. Sleep seemed to be my only escape, sleep and long rides in the car with my father. I liked the rides, they took me back to a happier time when I was loved and cared for and had no worries. But the paranoia crept in to ruin those times also. I sensed my father's impatience with me and felt that he wanted to get rid of me, that he wanted to kill me. What a terrible feeling! I lived in almost constant fear and that caused incredible anxiety.

The feelings of confusion and depression began in the spring of my first year at college. I was 19 years old; my girlfriend of a summer love went away to college in September, then broke up with me on Thanksgiving. The pressure was there: pressure of a love lost, pressure of college, pressure of growing up, pressure and confusion of being a child of divorce and many other pressures.

I felt so incredibly *guilty* when I was depressed. I felt that I shouldn't be depressed. People told me that I shouldn't feel depressed because I had so much going for me. That only helped me to feel more guilty. I wanted to know why I felt so terrible.

Having a logical mind, I said to myself, "If I feel this way, it must be because I did something wrong and I am being punished." I was raised with guilt and punishment. That was the kind of thinking I was involved in during the duration of the depression—guilt and fear of punishment. I now see how that type of thinking was self-perpetuating. After several months of deep paranoid depression, I remember feeling so guilty and saying to myself that I may have screwed up everything to this point in my life, but today is the first day of the rest of my life. I will start doing things better. I also started saying a holy rosary every night even though I felt so unworthy. Maybe, just maybe, God would have mercy on me and help me to get better.

I did start feeling better—much, much better. That is when I saw that *love* is the answer. This I still believe. But I had much to learn. I went soaring into the clouds and experienced what seemed to be the opposite of depression. I was high. I was sleeping little. I always slept some, though. I spent a lot of money, bounced checks, and had grandiose thoughts. The energy was incredible. I felt so good. In retrospect, however, I see that I was not peaceful. I was very short-tempered. If someone crossed me I often raged in anger at them. My biggest fights were with my parents, especially my mother, who was the one who left the house before the divorce. Anger which had been capped for years finally blew the lid off. I was very judgmental and had a hard time trying to stop talking. I felt extremely virile and felt no fear in approaching women. I met women very easily. It was hard for my parents and friends to cope with me, so I experienced a lot of rejection.

I was diagnosed with *manic depression* (bipolar disorder) in a ten minute interview with a psychiatrist provided by the school I was trying to re-enter. Looking back, it is clear that I did have the classic symptoms of what was called manic depression. Whether the interview lasted ten minutes or two hours, I believe the conclusion would have been the same, since they only looked at my behavioral symptoms. During depressions of other years, several other psychiatrists came to the same conclusion. They were convinced that it was a chemical imbalance and didn't look for any underlying reasons. They didn't look for causes: such as coming from a dysfunctional family system, being the child of a divorce, destructive methods of communication in the family, abandonment, improper nurturing, problems dealing with anger in the family, a generally unhealthy psychological living environment, etc., that might have caused the behavior I was exhibiting. I don't like labels, and much of my healing has come because of a refusal to accept the label called manic-depression. However, my healing might have never come if I had not eventually realized that there was a problem. I did have a certain type of extreme behavior—and thinking—and I did need help.

After working on my healing for a long period of time, I visited psychiatrists and therapists for less severe problems. The psychiatrists and therapists I went to said I was not a manic depressive. (One might say they undiagnosed me). ***Beware of labels. Don't accept a label! Labels are hard to get rid of. Do accept a diagnosis from a competent person (doctor or therapist) if they say that healing is needed.*** If you have been labeled, de-emphasize it. You are not a label. You are a person! Now—back to my story.

The dark cloud of depression reappeared again the next year. I was taken to a psychologist by my parents when I was very depressed and

18

paranoid. I wouldn't even speak to her because I was afraid that my parents just wanted to prove that I was crazy and commit me. I had no *trust* in the psychologist or in my parents. The psychologist said that there was nothing she could do if I would not talk. I wonder, aren't there other ways to gain a person's trust? I know I was a tough case, but again I was thrown out into the cold. Doesn't anyone out there like a challenge?

My mood swing pattern was repeated annually except for when I had a girlfriend who I felt loved me. During the time of our relationship, I went through a whole year without such drastic cycles. This experience made it clear to me that one of my problems was a *lack of love* in my life.

Over the course of about 15 years, I battled with bipolar depression. Each time though, as I became more *aware* of things that influenced my cycles and applied healing methods I had learned, the cycles became less and less extreme.

I had taken lithium for a time and antidepressants, too. I can testify that antidepressants do work. I resisted them for years and did not believe in them. However, I did give them a sure test the last time I felt myself slipping into a major depression. I took Prozac, tapped into my support network and totally avoided what felt like a sure depression coming.

My support included: going for therapy, seeing a psychiatrist for the medication, attending a Depressive/Manic-Depressive Support Group, and opening my heart to friends I knew I could trust. Having previously taken antidepressants, I knew myself and my cycles. I knew how I responded to medication. Hence, when I saw that I was beyond what would normally be my depression time, I stopped taking the Prozac. My psychiatrist recommended that I continue the Prozac, but she did not threaten or coerce me or fill me with fear concerning my decision. She respected my decision and supported me. I respect her greatly for that! Fortunately this psychiatrist was not real pushy like others I'd seen. Please note that I was under this psychiatrist's care when I tapered off the medication. I also continued with counseling to work through the problems that were troubling me and causing my brain chemistry to go out of whack.

I have never been severely depressed since, and have not taken medication again. One should not use this approach without an excellent support network and a substantial amount of self-knowledge about the course of one's cycles in the past. Alternative coping methods must be in place before giving up medication! Also, be sure to read the *Warning* section at the beginning of this book and Dr. Peter Breggin's book listed in Appendix B.

When I started getting depressed that last time (1989), there were two major stressful events to be noted. My father died six months prior to the depression and my girlfriend of one and a half years was breaking up with me. Consequently, I went for help right away.

Going back in time (mid—to late 1970's), after I had my initial bouts of depression and euphoria, I was treated with medication. I took it for a while, but did not buy into the diagnosis that I had a chemical imbalance in my brain and would have to take medication for the rest of my life. Also, I did research on the medication and found it had side-effects that could be harmful. Hence, I chose to seek other solutions.

Some medications can be like aspirin. They treat the symptoms, but generally do not get to the root of the problem. *It seems that medication dulls our emotional pain. When the pain is dulled, we are often no longer motivated to ask: What is causing this pain? What might this pain be trying to teach me? What do I need to change in my life to stop the pain?* Pain can be a powerful motivator to change what needs to be changed! Take away the pain and you may take away the motivation to change what *really* needs to be changed to stop the pain. I decided I would rather have the pain and learn, than live medicated.

As a result of my decision, I have learned much about the causes of my problems. I have also learned many alternative ways to reduce symptoms and facilitate healing. Hopefully these will make your (or your loved ones) suffering less. These methods have had very positive results and have no negative side-effects. Keep in mind, some people may choose to take medication and seek other ways to help themselves as well.

Looking back over the years, as I was going through the horrors of depression, paranoia, and the high side of the bipolar disorder (as it is now termed), I did a lot of digging to find answers. I read many *self-help books,* found *support groups,* listened to *talk shows* on the radio, and went to *therapy.* Any time I found something that dealt with depression or bipolar, I grabbed it and read it, keeping what I thought was worthwhile and discarding the rest.

As already mentioned, I no longer experience deep depressions or extreme highs and have put the paranoia to rest. Of course I do experience times of moderate ups and downs which most everyone experiences during the course of life's events. I realize that recovery is a life-long process and there is much more to be learned and to *become.* My recovery has taught me that as I get in touch with my real self, my deep inner self and the purpose for which God has made me—not what society or friends or relatives say I *should* do or be—I become happier, more peaceful, and fulfilled.

In my story, I often felt as if my family pointed the finger at me. I was the problem. I was the one who got depressed. I was the one who was different. They were all OK.

It was so consoling and made so much sense to me when I watched John Bradshaw's video "On The Family." Bradshaw views the family as a system. He clearly explained that depression, alcoholism, drug addiction, and many other addictive behaviors are indicators of a problem in *The Family System.* They are not just an individual's problem. In my opinion, the person who suffers from depression or manic depression is often behaving quite normally, given the circumstances of their life and childhood history. In order to heal, it is important to understand our family history, the role we play, and how we got set up in that role. We must also form relationships with healthy people and healthy families to learn new behavior and healthy ways of thinking and relating.

A friend of mine has been hit hard in her family with manic-depression. Hence, she also has lived with and aided an immediate family member suffering from these symptoms. My friend has researched and studied this diagnosis, together with its causes and treatment. I believe she said it so clearly when she said, "Manic Depression is just the smoke. The huge mood swings are just an indicator of unresolved mental, emotional, and spiritual issues—which is the fire." Let's deal with these issues and not just medicate the symptoms.

Another friend of mine was diagnosed as a manic depressive. I met her at a Codependents Anonymous meeting. She said, "I believe that taking drugs keeps us from getting to the feelings that we need to get to in order to work through the hurt and heal." This woman had stopped taking drugs, was working through her emotional pain and was healing quite well. "What courage!" I thought. However, when pain and/or symptoms are very extreme, medication may be needed. It may not be possible to work through deeper issues until the pain and other symptoms are lessened with the help of medication—at least temporarily.

> **"Manic depression is just the smoke. The huge mood swings are just an indicator of unresolved mental, emotional, and spiritual issues—which is the fire."** Let's deal with these issues and not just medicate the symptoms.

Don't minimize the pain! It is easy to minimize our pain with

The Unseen Cross

I said to a woman I know, "Sometimes I feel guilty that I get so depressed when I look at a person who is severely, physically handicapped. He has a reason to get depressed and yet he is coping."

This wise woman replied, "It is easier for the person who is physically handicapped. It is clear that he is unfortunate. People look at him, feel for him and want to help him. Your cross can't be seen. Depression can't be seen. There is little compassion for you, since people don't even know that you are suffering." A cross of such intense loneliness and hopelessness is a very great cross indeed.

I never forgot what that woman told me years ago. It helped to validate my feelings. I felt that someone understood, at least a little. That eased the pain and guilt, at least somewhat.

> **To bear such a cross, and to rise above it, is to move a mountain!**

Anyone who attempts this should be congratulated. And attempt we must! The good news is that many people *do* understand now, since so many suffer from depression. All due respect to the physically handicapped—both are great crosses. The point is that we should not minimize our problems by comparing ourselves to others. *The pain that each individual feels is real for them* and they must learn how to either work through it or live with it.

A note to doctors, therapists, family members, and friends of the person suffering from Depression or Bipolar Depressive mood swings:

Please remember that I am more than a depressive.

I am more than a manic depressive,
a bipolar depressive,
or any other label you might like to affix to me.

I am a person.

I am a human being,
capable of loving and being loved
who has suffered from large mood swings
which have been labeled manic depression.

I am able to see and touch and feel and think.

Yes, I, like you, am a feeling person.

I am a human being
who needs to be respected,
just as you do,
who needs to be loved,
just as you do.

I need to be considered 'OK,'
just as you do.

I need to be accepted 'as I am,'
just as you do—Maybe even more so.

I have ups and downs,
just as you do.

They may be higher highs
and lower lows
than yours.

Can you imagine the pain of such low lows?

Can you imagine?

And can you imagine the pain of being alienated?
By being "labeled as different" than
"normal" people?

If you must see me as different,
please see me as the extra-sensitive person I am.

A sensitive person may have higher highs and lower lows
than the average person,
but he or she can feel many things that
much of humanity with dulled senses cannot.

I can hear the birds sing,
see the sun rise,
notice the diamond glistening
on the blade of grass
as the sun shines on the early morning dew.

In feeling so much,
I can feel the pain of our suffering sisters
and brothers in the human family.

I hear the children cry,
The elderly moan,
The hungry cry out for food,
The lonely and depressed cry out for love.

I see the stars laughing in the sky.

The squirrels playing.

The bright red cardinals singing
with the joy of heaven.

The yellow roses.

Puffy white clouds.

*I realize that because I am very sensitive
I can get angry easily too—high.*

Depressed easily too—low.

*I realize how important it is to learn how to channel
the gift of my sensitivity away from fear
and toward positive things.*

*To learn to calm myself if I get flighty ideas and comfort myself if I feel
myself getting depressed.*

*I'm in the process of discovering how to
manage my beautiful sensitivity.
Please be patient with me as I learn how to esteem myself,
calm myself, and love myself.*

Thank you.

Questions

1.   Is not a classical distinguishing feature of a manic depressive the fact that he or she has abnormal mood swings (ups and downs)?

2.   Doesn't everyone have ups and downs—depressing times and happy times?

3.   How do we distinguish between a highly emotional person (whose ups and downs are exaggerated) and the true manic depressive?

4.   Does a true manic depressive exist? Or are we all hurting, even those who label us and *treat* us?

5.   Could it be that some are just hurting more than others and so, need more love and more tools to cope? Could it be that these people have an even greater need to be accepted, valued, and included rather than labeled and set apart?

6.   Are there ways other than taking medication to alter one's brain chemistry and correct any chemical imbalances that one may have? Are there ways to accomplish this that do not have the side-effects that medications have? If so, what are they?

7.   Are not emotion and creativity the driving forces behind innovation, great works of art, science, music, and philosophical advances? In short, aren't strong emotion and creativity behind all great works? Many great minds in the past were people who were considered outcasts and not appreciated in their time. Most were driven by strong emotion and high creative abilities just like the ones who are now being labeled manic-depressives and are too often *only* being medicated. I wonder what we are doing to the creative future of the world by this response?

I believe those who are called manic depressives are often our poets, our artists, our Mozarts, and our prophets. We are society's feelers, the sensitive ones. We are ones who often are the first to feel and express the things going wrong in our upbringing, our society, and in the way we relate to one another. Let us listen to the sensitive ones, instead of only medicating them—often to cover up our own hurts and mistakes. Let us *awaken* before it is too late.

I say thank you, my sensitive brothers and sisters, and wish this for us all:

May our depressions turn to joy

and our

euphoria be traded for peace.

Chapter 2

SYMPTOMS

of

Depression and Bipolar Disorder

M ost people suffer mildly from various symptoms of depression from time to time. However, it is when these symptoms are extreme, when they cause us not to be able to function, when they are consuming or ruining our lives, when they continue over an extended period of time that the symptoms are to be taken as a sign of a serious depression.

Of course, even mild depression should be addressed and dealt with. In this way, a potentially deep or clinical depression may be avoided, and one can enjoy a fuller and happier life.

Stress/Pressure
internal and/or external

Healthy person.	**Depressed person.**	**High person.**
Energy/self expression in balance	Energy/self expression compressed, held in too much	Energy/self expression released too much, too fast.

Spring Illustration of Bipolar Disorder

27

The chapter "TOOLS: For the Depressed Person and the Person Who is Hyper or High" may be applied by *anyone* to achieve a happier, more peaceful state of mind and to gain emotional balance. The following pages contain a list of symptoms of depression. A list of symptoms for the high side of bipolar depression (bipolar disorder) follows that. A person with bipolar depression experiences debilitating mood swings from deep depression, passes through a normal point and then goes into an episode of uncontrollable elation, restlessness, racing thoughts, and delusions of grandeur. An individual may not have all the symptoms listed, but the more one has, and the greater the severity, often the worse the depression (or mania for the High-Side symptoms).

There are asterisks next to the symptoms that are most severe. A person who is experiencing several or all of the severe symptoms—or many of the others listed—and who has been depressed for longer than two weeks would be wise to seek some professional help. There is no special order to the list of symptoms which begins on the following page.

<u>Below is some space to note symptoms you may have:</u>

Symptoms of Depression

Pendulum

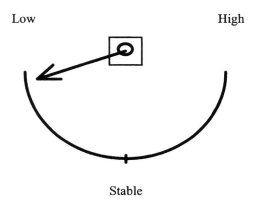

Low   High

Stable

1.   Little or no interest in usual activities.

2.   Consistent lack of energy. Feeling of weakness.

3. *   Feeling hopeless. (Saying, "Things will never get better." "I'll never be happy.")

4.   Feelings of guilt, all or most of the time. An unwarranted guilt. Feeling terribly guilty over a small thing.

5.   Feeling sad all of the time.

6.   Thoughts are dominated by negativity. Not able to see good in life, others, or self.

7. *   Change in appetite. Over-eating or losing too much weight.

8. *   Sleep disturbance. Too much or too little sleep.

9. *   Thoughts of suicide, or thoughts like "I just wish I weren't here, or wasn't born."

10.*   Inability to function at home, at work, or a significant drop in grades at school.

11.   Lack of interest or no interest at all in sex.

12.   Extreme feelings of anxiety, for no apparent reason.

13.   Feeling worthless or feeling like a failure.

14.   Excessive crying or unable to cry at all.

15.   Feeling afraid all or much of the time. Panic attacks.

16.   Afraid of spending money. Much more conservative than usual.

17.   Emotionally numb. Like nothing really matters. Can't feel happy for others. When others are suffering, its hard to feel compassion for them.

18.*   Avoiding social functions and friends. Turning more to isolation.

19.   Inability to concentrate, study, or think clearly. A feeling of being in a fog, cloudy headed.

20.   Indecisiveness. For example: can't even decide which clothes to wear.

21.   Inability to give or receive love.

22.   No feeling of joy in life.

23.   Little or no appreciation of beauty.

24.*   Engaging in self-destructive activities such as self-blame, bingeing on food, consuming excessive amounts of alcohol or drugs, etc. Overly self-critical. The more self-destructive the activities, the more severe the problem.

25.   Low self-esteem.

26.   The conscience is over-sensitive—it is in control.

27.   Sense of freedom and personal power to direct one's life is suppressed.

28.   Feeling distant from God.

29.   Over cautious. Afraid to take risks.

30.   Seeming to be humble and submissive while often burning with anger, but afraid to express it.

31.   Exaggerated thoughts: Self-pity: "I'm *so* bad, nobody can help me." This can be a kind of grandiosity or pride, hidden in a posture of powerlessness. An extreme kind of thinking.

32.   Little or no self-expression or creativity.

33.   Anger. Depression has been termed "anger turned inward."

34.   Person often becomes very inward and doesn't talk much. Although, some people might even talk more.

35.   Not able to find pleasure in anything.

36.   Feeling alone and isolated. Inability to feel emotional connection.

37.   Change in hygiene. Less interest in keeping clean. Lack of interest in personal appearance. This is one of the earlier symptoms of depression.

38.   Bowel disturbance—often constipation occurs with depression.

39.   Dehydration. Signs of this are: dry or chapped lips, always feeling thirsty, dry skin, constipation, dryness in the nose, dark yellow urine, and dry eyes.

40.*   Obsessive thinking—can't seem to stop thinking about something or someone. This can send brain chemistry out of whack. Address this quickly!

41.   Aches and pains. The body and mind are one. When the mind aches, often, so does the body. Strange and seemingly hard to understand aches and pains may appear in various areas of the body. Sometimes they even seem to mysteriously move to different areas at random.

Often mental depression is masked by aches and pains. It is somatized and seems to be experienced more in the body than in the mind. It can also be masked by physical sickness—colds, flu, etc.

42.   Physical numbness and/or tingling may be experienced in different areas of the body.

There are different kinds of depression. Mild and acute depressions are painful, but they offer a time for growth and reevaluation of our lives. Chronic depression, however, is disabling and we should be sure to get help to deal with it. A person who has the symptoms with the asterisks next to them is most likely experiencing chronic depression. One might also be experiencing chronic depression with several of the other symptoms to a sharper degree. A great intensity of emotional pain and an inability to cope with life are two good measures that point to chronic depression.

A person who is depressed might feel something like this.

32

Symptoms of the High Side (For Bipolar)

The pendulum swings
Balance must be achieved

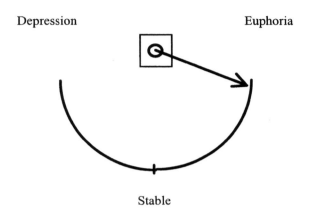

Depression   Euphoria

Stable

Note: There are asterisks next to the more serious symptoms. If you are experiencing these, seek professional help.

1. A feeling of euphoria. Feeling too happy, for no reason.

2. Anger turned outward. Short with people. May also rage or yell and scream at people.

3. A feeling that you can love well. Feeling very lovable, like all the girls/guys love me.

4. Self-indulgence, overdoing things that feel good.

5. A somewhat deceptive feeling of high self-esteem, much self-confidence.

6. The conscience is now suppressed (you feel like you can do no wrong).

7. Self-control is let loose—it flies (see the "spring" illustration at the beginning of this chapter). Self-control has gone from too much

(depression) to too little (high). The jack-in-the-box toy can teach us something about bipolar depression.

8.   Feeling as if you can do anything, omnipotent, strong.

9. * Grandiose thoughts—"I can build a plane in one week." Some people think they are Jesus Christ or are a god of some sort. Often, these people were religious to begin with.

10. Feeling close to God if religious (sometimes even when not religious).

11. Strong sexual appetite.

12. Feeling as if you love life. Everything is wonderful (in an unrealistic way).

13. Feeling overly hopeful (in an unrealistic way).

14. Spending a lot of money. Getting into debt, wasting money and may bounce checks.

15. Pride, a feeling of being better than others.

16. Uncaring, not aware that your actions might be hurting someone else.

17. Feeling sensitive and alive.

18. Self-expression/creativity released.

19.* Overactive, taking on too many activities. Never resting, until exhausted.

20. Talk a lot. Pressured speech. Always feel I have to say something. Endless talking at times.

21.* Sleep disturbance—don't usually sleep enough. May stay up all night because there is a feeling of so much energy. If not sleeping at all for more than one or two nights at a time, seek professional help.

22. Bowel disturbance. Going often. Bowel movements are too loose or diarrhea.

23.* Suicide—If entertaining thoughts of suicide, seek professional help immediately! Keep in mind, what you really want to kill is the pain, not yourself!

24.* Hallucinations—If hallucinating, seeing things that are not there or hearing voices when no one is there, seek professional help.

25.* Destructive tendencies toward self or others.

Note: The preceding symptoms are in no particular order of severity. If experiencing the symptoms with the asterisks next to them, seek professional help. If for any reason you can't or won't seek professional help, at least talk to a friend who cares about you. Don't try to go it alone!

** <u>Bipolar Depression</u> **

** <u>The low side and high side compared</u> **

What do both swings have in common?
They seem so opposite!

ANGER	Depression is anger turned inward, mania is anger turned outward.
GRANDIOSITY	A kind of pride. Either I'm "so good" and wonderful and can do almost anything (high). Or I am "so bad" that no one can help me. (low).
SELF-CONTROL IMBALANCE	Too much or too little self-control.
EXTREMES	The person thinks and lives in extremes. He or she has a strong response to stimuli. In short, she or he is a very

sensitive person with strong emotions. These are gifts and if disciplined and channeled can be a great asset to the individual and to society.

SLEEP DISTURBANCE   Too much sleep or too little.

Whoever gave manic depression the much gentler label of "Bipolar Depression" seems to be right on the mark. For it seems that the low side and the high side (although apparently so different) are both depression which is expressing itself using two different masks. The root of the depression usually involves a damaged self-esteem.

The damaged self-esteem can be easily seen in the person who is feeling depressed, but does not seem to be true of the person who is feeling euphoric. However, the veil of the euphoric person is quickly shed if the person is crossed. The euphoric person who is crossed gets angry very fast and usually has very little of the tolerance and patience which are characteristic of a truly happy person with high self-esteem. Some things that need to be addressed in the *healing* of a person suffering from either depression or bipolar depression are: low self-esteem, anger, and self-hatred. The *symptoms* may be addressed and dealt with. However, I believe that real healing involves a process of learning to esteem and love ourselves and others properly.

Things which lessen the swing of the pendulum on both sides:

- LOVE
- FAITH
- ACCEPTANCE
- TOLERANCE
- CONSISTENCY
- MEDITATION
- NATURE
- LETTING GO
- FEELING & EXPRESSING OUR FEELINGS
- PHYSICAL EXERCISE

Hopefully our families and friends will provide these as we struggle in coping with our mood swings. We must however, learn how to esteem and love ourselves. For if we need something outside of us to feel OK, then we

36

are like puppets dangling from the strings of others who control our happiness.

Depression   Euphoria

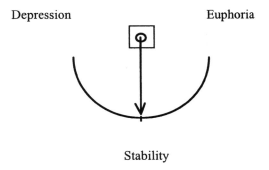

Stability

• Love lifts the depressed person
• Love calms the hyper and angry person
• Love——Just love

Please keep in mind, the love needed for stability is *immense* and most often cannot come from one person alone! However, every individual person's love matters.

Chapter 3

CAUSES

Individual and Societal

O ften there is no one simple explanation for the cause of depression. The road to health is like putting the pieces of a puzzle together. During the searching process, I would occasionally find a piece of the puzzle and put it into my life to make a more healthy and whole picture. Everyone's puzzle is different, but there are some pieces that seem to be common to many of us. It is on these, and the ones that fit for myself, that I will focus.

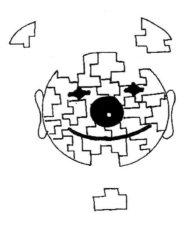

It's like putting the pieces of a puzzle together

I said there wasn't any one cause, but if I were to pick one sentence that sums up almost everything, it would be the following:

> **The cause of most depression and bipolar depression is a general lack of proper LOVE and caring in the environment in which we live (especially our early childhood nurturing.)**

Depression can be caused by physiological factors, such as an improperly functioning thyroid. Therefore, a thorough physical checkup should be the first course of action. However, don't stop there, even if something is found. *Our emotions and unhealthy thoughts often contribute to, or are the direct cause of, our physical problems.*

Let's look at some circumstances that can cause or contribute to the cause of depression. There are certain obvious ones, such as: loss of a loved one, loss of job, divorce and major illness. There are also *stress producers* that are not so obvious. One might take a bucket of water and dump it into a sink to fill it, or one might let water *drip* for a long enough time and it will also fill the sink.

It is the *elusive* dripping, I have found, that contributes to the cause of my depressions; the not so obvious, cumulative effect of many little pressures, (and some big ones) which, at first glance, don't appear to exist. However, in my past, before they were recognized, they not only filled the bucket, but overflowed into some horrible, deep and long depressions. Upon careful examination and observation, and with the help of a good *plumber*, the dripping has now been discovered and dealt with. I will list some of these things, the ones found to be the droplets as well as the bucketfuls.

SELF-PRESSURES
(Internal pressures or struggles)

Emotional Immaturity

We let our joy and happiness be controlled by our circumstances instead of from within, and of course, from God.

Lack of Forgiveness

Holding on to hurt and anger instead of confronting the cause of the anger and dealing with it, then forgiving the offender, and letting it go. We must have the compassion to forgive ourselves as well as others.

Negative and Critical Thinking

This triggers chemical reactions in our brain that dump *toxins* into our systems causing a *chemical imbalance* and possibly depression. The chemical imbalances tend to perpetuate more negative thinking. Thus, a negative cycle is set up. Disciplining one's mind to think positive and encouraging thoughts helps to break that cycle. We must feed our brain by reading encouraging books and spending time with people who are positive and encouraging.

Polarized Thinking

Polarized thinking is thinking in the extremes. Some people see things as *all or nothing*, black or white, right or wrong. When in fact, most of real life is not *all or nothing*, rather somewhere in-between. Does thinking in extremes sound familiar? Does behavior in extremes sound familiar? Manic-Depressive behavior is certainly behavior in the extremes. The sufferer is either flying high or deep in depression. *Uni-polar depression* is an extreme only on the *low* end. Behavior in extremes is certainly *fueled* by thinking in extremes (and/or extreme thinking). Could thinking in extremes or *extreme thinking* contribute to or even cause one's brain chemistry to go out of balance? Likewise, could ending extreme thinking and learning to think in more balanced healthy ways help correct brain chemistry imbalances? The answers to these questions – certainly! Polarized thinking must be addressed and changed by the person in recovery from depression or bipolar depression. Styles of thinking are usually learned in our families of origin. Counseling methods such as *cognitive therapy* and *rational emotive therapy* (RET) work to heal these kinds of thinking problems.

Catastrophic Thinking

When someone is late, you assume that they were in an accident. That is catastrophic thinking. Simply put, catastrophic thinking is *assuming the worst*. A healthier thought might be to assume that they just hit traffic or got a late start. Catastrophic thinking can feed depression. The *worry* habit can also feed depression and bipolar. For the person who wishes to heal from depression or bipolar, these poor thinking habits must be replaced by the habit of *optimism*.

Imbalance

Our needs—*mind, body, spirit, social* and *emotional* needs are often not all being met. Some may be getting met much more than others, thus creating an imbalance.

Stress

External circumstances, or internal struggles can cause stress. If you put a healthy person in an unhealthy atmosphere, he or she will be affected and may become unhealthy. According to a study of the effect of stress on people suffering from bipolar depression the results were as follows: **Persons with very high stress had a 4.53 times (that's 453%) greater chance of relapse than those without high stress.** *American Journal of Psychiatry* September 90 (p1194) (5). Too much work or even too much fun (good things) can be stressful. Change causes stress. Some stress is needed, as well as change. However, too much change, too fast, leads to too much stress, or distress, which leads to breakdown of some sort in our body/mind system. *Stress management* **is a major factor in dealing with depression and bipolar depression.**

Client: Why did I have to wait in your waiting room for 2 hours?
Psychiatrist: That was your stress test.

Giving Burnout

Can you pour water out of an empty cup? When a person gives too much and doesn't take care of himself or herself, burnout can occur. We cannot *only* be pouring out to others; we must allow people to fill us too. Otherwise we will wind up empty and depressed. (See chapter 7 for ways to avoid burnout.)

Anger

We are often not in touch with our anger or its causes. Too many people don't allow themselves to feel angry. Suppressing anger causes us either physical or psychological problems. It's like pushing a beach ball under water and letting it go. It always pops up somewhere. Anger is not wrong or sinful; it's just a feeling. What is important is what we do with our anger. Holding onto anger and holding it in can cause brain chemistry to go out of whack. See the section about dealing with anger in the TOOLS chapter.

Inaction

Depression can be caused by *inaction*, by not doing what we are called to do, not doing what our inner self calls us to do. An example of what we may need to do is stand up for ourselves when someone has hurt us or to stand up for others when we see an injustice.

Commitment   Human beings *need* to feel secure to remain healthy. But how can we feel secure when someone leaves at the first sign of trouble? That someone might be ourselves. This attitude must stop. Learn to hang in there with relationships, even when things get tough, and work things through, except, of course, in cases of abuse. Where abuse is experienced and confronted, but still continues, it is wise to get out of the situation.

Unrealistic   When the mind realizes that its unrealistic dreams won't be
Dreams   met, the body shuts down; the mind shuts down too.

Guilt   There is *appropriate* and *inappropriate* guilt. When we do something wrong, it is healthy to feel some guilt. Guilt helps us change our behavior. However, a gnawing guilt that seems to never leave, and/or is much more than is warranted for the situation, is unhealthy and may lead to depression.

Control   Some mechanisms people use to control us and that we use to control others, either consciously or, more often, subconsciously, are: guilt, sex, jealousy, fear, abandonment, ultimatums, weakness, servitude and withholding of praise. Using these methods to manipulate and control people is destructive to our (and others') mental health. It is not a question of *blame*. This is often a dysfunctional type of thinking and control that was handed down from generation to generation on a *subconscious* level. We often do these things and are unaware of it because our motivations are not on a conscious level . If not uncovered and brought to a conscious level (through counseling), if left uncorrected, this dysfunctional relating will continue down the ages. The biblical depiction of this is "the sins of the fathers." We must take control of ourselves and our own lives, and not let others pull our strings. To *influence* others is OK, assuming it is in their best interest. However, to *control* others either overtly or covertly is not healthy, especially if it is predominantly for our own selfish interests and/or to their detriment.

Child Abuse   This is often overlooked. People think of child abuse only as the obvious physical abuse that leaves marks on a child's body. However, there are other much more *subtle, covert* forms of abuse that can be just as devastating to the child. The effect of abuse often doesn't show up until much later in life. It may surface as depressive or manic depressive behavior.

Looking at the dysfunctional environment that many of us were raised in, it is clear to me that this less than nurturing environment can set us up for manic depressive type of behavior.

I am amazed at the subtleties of the form of mistreatment that many endure. Some hurts are overt and obvious. Others are a kind of slow and unobvious torture. Our parents deny it because, I'm sure, they believed that what they did was right. It is also clear to me that it is not a case of blame. Our parents didn't give us proper nurturing because their parents didn't give them proper nurturing, and our grandparent's parents did the same with them. Fortunately, there are those who have received therapy and much new information that their parents never had. For those, the abuse will stop with themselves and not be passed down to *their* children.

Research has found that *abuse changes brain chemistry*. There is continued research being done on the subject. The good news is that **love changes brain chemistry too**. Abuse causes chemical imbalances in our brain. Love—real and consistent love—restores that balance over time.

It has been found that when a person is chronically abused, pain cells in their brain cluster together. When an event occurs later in life that triggers these pain cells to activate, the pain of the past is relived. The pain can be very severe! An event that is similar to what the original abuser did, said, or looked like, could act as a trigger. The only way out of the pain is to face the shame, feel the hurt and anger and do the healthy grieving we need to do to heal. This is best accomplished in therapy and support groups.

45

Oh the pain
That our families cause us (and we them)
The "Unknown" pain
Greater than 1000 torture chambers
Chambers well conceived
Hardly even able to be seen!
Yet so devastating
But Alas
Ah
The indelible human spirit
How it endures
Even one day
Awakens
And through the power of "will"
Breaks the chains
And sets itself
free

Body Chemistry

Hormones, and the side-effects of drugs taken can cause depression. Emotional response to a physical illness can cause depression. Emotional response to any traumatic life experience can cause our body and/or brain chemistry to become imbalanced.

Drugs

Alcohol is a depressant. It may help us to feel better for a while by relaxing us and releasing our inhibitions. But then the effect wears off and we usually feel worse than before we drank. Caffeine and nicotine are stimulants that may give us a kick, but for every bound there is usually a rebound. Any of these or other drugs may throw our body chemistry off. The harmful effects of such drugs (both the physical and psychological harm) are well documented. They contribute to both depression and bipolar depression. Avoid alcohol, caffeine, nicotine and any substances that have either a stimulant or depressant effect.

Stay away from non-prescription drugs and carefully evaluate the pros and cons of prescription medication as well. Read labels and ask your doctor what the possible side-effects are before using medication.

Isolation

We are social beings, and spending too much time alone can lead to depression. Living alone can be very stressful for many people. Why live alone when there are so many people who would love to live with us?

Pride

Often, people have too much pride to ask for help. This can lead to isolation and either cause or intensify depression. Some people have too much pride to admit that they are hurting. People who have a very successful *outward image* are often a victim of this trap. Let's bite the bullet and reach out.

Inordinate Desire

Persistence in desiring something or someone we cannot or should not have is an example of inordinate desire. A good barometer to determine if one is having an inordinate desire is the following: Does my desire go against nature? Another is: Is this desire ultimately bringing me peace and joy, or is it bringing me pain and misery?

Relationship Addiction

Since many (or even most) people who suffer with depression or manic depression have roots of these diseases in childhood, it stands to reason that such people are vulnerable to relationship addiction.

Most of us who have suffered from these diseases have suffered from *love deprivation* as children. Either we were loved and nurtured poorly or we suffered because of a parent who was either abusive or not present physically or emotionally. The following are some examples of this: a father who was away on business all the time, a mother who was an alcoholic or sickaholic, a mother who controlled her children by using guilt, abandonment, fear and manipulation, or a father who continually criticized his children and rarely, if ever, complimented and affirmed them.

47

Relationship Addict. (cont.)   Such love deprived people *hunger* for the love they never received as children and are very vulnerable to relationship problems later on in life.

Some symptoms of relationship addiction are:

1) always picking and staying with people who hurt us and/or don't respect us.
2) feeling that "I can't live without him/her."
3) getting very depressed (or high) if the relationship breaks off or is not what we would like it to be.
4) staying in a relationship even though we are always feeling short-changed (always giving, but not getting).

If you suspect that you might be a relationship addict I highly recommend that you read, *Love Gone Wrong* by Thomas A. Whiteman, Ph.D. and Randy Petersen. This is an excellent book with self-tests to see if there is a problem and solutions to get out of unhealthy or addictive relationships.

By *relationships* I am not only talking about romance. It could be a friend (same or opposite sex) or even a family member relationship. Don't take this lightly. Before I realized I was addicted to a relationship, I could not sleep more than 3–5 hours a night for several months. That wreaked havoc on my biochemistry and on my body. While disengaging from the relationship, I felt like a drug addict in withdrawal. After I'd stayed away from her, my sleep returned to normal. Fortunately solid recovery tools brought sleep back rather quickly after we separated.

Some solutions to relationship addiction can be found in the Tools, Human Needs, and The Power of Faith chapters of the book you are now reading. What we need is to be loved properly. We need to spend time with people who can do that. We must build our self-esteem. In general, we must love and nurture ourselves and let others do that too. Above all, I believe we must have a relationship with God. Usually *any addiction* is a false substitute used to fill a deep spiritual hunger to have a fulfilling relationship with God and *healthy* loving connection with our fellow brothers and sisters of humanity.

> **Usually *any addiction* is a false substitute used to fill a deep spiritual hunger to have a fulfilling relationship with God and *healthy* loving connection with our fellow brothers and sisters of humanity.**

CURRENT SOCIETAL PRESSURES
(or external pressures)

Competition   People working against one another instead of together.

The News   The news is an unbalanced view of the world. A high percentage of what is broadcasted is bad news, when in fact the world is full of good news too. How can we feel good when we are absorbing all of this bad news?

Peer Pressure   People want to fit in. We want to be considered part of a group, to belong. We want to be accepted. This can be a very positive force or it can be a negative one. The positive force can come from a healthy loving community with good morals, values, and a respect for individuality. Negative peer pressure comes from people or groups who try to exploit a person's need to be accepted. These people or groups often have a need to control other people for their own selfish and often vengeful motives. To protect ourselves and our children from such influences—*cults*, etc.—there are several things we can do:
1. Bring up our children to love and follow the truth, even if it is sometimes painful.
2. Teach our children healthy questioning, to question and test everything that they hear. Don't just believe everything.

49

Peer Pressure (Cont.)

Filter it, using what their parents taught them, as well as other proven sources of moral guidance—like The Bible.
3. Don't give our children a reason to have to sell themselves to be accepted. Provide an *accepting* loving home environment for them.
4. Encourage and teach our children how to stand on their own and never to compromise their values for anyone. Most of society's greatest minds were people who differed in opinion from the crowd and had the courage to stand on their own.
5. Present healthy alternatives to destructive groups. Encourage children to get into wholesome groups. Many churches have youth groups and many high schools have supervised activities. We can encourage children to join sports teams, art clubs, a musical organization or numerous other healthy activities.
6. Address our children's needs. Ask children and young adults what their needs are. Don't just assume you know. Remember, boredom often leads to mischievousness.

Loss of Loved One

This is listed as one of the highest stress producers on most stress charts. The loss can be due to death or divorce. It can also be due to someone who is loved or cherished that leaves us—a breakup with a boyfriend or girlfriend for example. This loss can precipitate depression.

Unhealthy Communication Styles

Many of us grew up in families where there were very unhealthy methods of communication. Some of these unhealthy communication methods are: Sarcasm, ignoring, blaming, denying another their right to have and express their feelings, being told "you're too sensitive," being *shamed* for being yourself, being told you are stupid, being told you are a mental retard, discounting a persons good deeds, making one feel guilty, hurtful teasing, put-downs, name-calling, betraying trusts, being told your thinking is wrong when it is just different, and doing everything for someone to the point that the other person is helpless. These things wreak havoc on a persons self-esteem and can lead to depression.

Emotions not Integrated   When we were children we had many conflicting emotions. Emotions of love and hate, emotions of joy and of anger. We needed to be accepted and loved with *all* of our emotions. If we were only loved when we were nice and not when we were sad or angry, or if we were rejected when we were angry, then we have not integrated our anger into ourselves as being OK. This may lead to problems with anger and depression or bipolar when in adulthood. In the TOOLS chapter, look for *Emotional Integration* to see how one can heal in this area.

Job Loss   Losing a job can wreak havoc on one's self-esteem. Our culture is very much a *doing* and *production-oriented* culture. As a result of this, many peoples' self-esteem is intimately connected with their job. This brings about the attitude: If I don't have work, if I am not doing, if I am not producing, and especially if I am not making money, then I am not worth much. This simply is not true. A person is priceless just because they exist! However, there is also the stress that comes with not being able to pay the bills. An excellent book for helping with the job search is called *What Color is Your Parachute?*—by Bolles (See Appendix B). There are also job support groups available which are very helpful. Can't find one? Start one.

Threat of Job Loss   An immense amount of stress comes with being in a company (and culture) that is constantly laying people off. I imagine it to be a little like being in Aushwitz. The Jews who were imprisoned never knew, when they were taken somewhere else, if they were going to be executed or not. It has been said that the *stress from the unknown* was so bad that some wished death would happen, just to end the extraordinary pain of impending doom.

Let's go easy on one another and on ourselves. Let us support one another in this time of tremendous stress in which we live. We would also do well to esteem ourselves through a source other than our jobs. This will help us to keep the job or to cope if we lose it.

51

Work

My friend Carl said to me, "Paul, I think I know why so many people are depressed." Curious, I asked "Why?" Carl said, "Because they hate their jobs. How can you not be depressed when you spend 8 hours or more a day doing something you hate?" It's hard to argue with that point. I believe many people get caught in jobs they don't like because either they are there only for the money, the benefits are good, or they are afraid of—or unmotivated to—change. If one cannot or will not change one's job, there are *creative* ways to find joy in one's work. We should seek them rather than get depressed.

Materialism

Emphasis is put on "things" instead of people

Creativity

In many places, creativity is not valued in our world today. The quick buck has a much higher value. The creative craftsman has been replaced by the assembly line, yet human beings *need* to create.

Our Worth

Our worth is based on what we produce or what we own instead of who we are.

Debt

Our concept of living in debt, instead of saving joyfully for what we want, robs us of joy and causes or feeds depression. This makes us feel enslaved and usually contributes to our stress.

Divorce

Where do we go for support if we have no family? What does a child do when his or her parents are fighting against each other and using the child as a weapon? Divorce can have devastating effects on children extending even into their adult years. My parents were divorced when I was 15. Their divorce left me with immense fears of abandonment and a lot of insecurity and fear in my own relationships. Divorce often leaves children with much anger, depression, feelings of guilt, and confusion as well.

Alcoholism	Alcoholism is rampant in our society today. Alcoholics often have huge mood swings—from elation to despair. That certainly fits into the depression and bipolar depression symptoms doesn't it?

A study was done on alcoholics and manic-depressives. It was hard to tell the difference between these two groups since their behaviors were so similar. The affects of alcohol often live on in families long after the cork is put in the bottle.

Children of alcoholics are usually filled with anger because of the environment they grew up in. Children and adult children of alcoholics often suffer from depressive and bipolar depressive mood swings. Hence, it would be a good idea to examine your family history for the affects of alcohol on yourself and your family. This can be accomplished in therapy. |
| **Change** | We live in a society of *rapid change*. I believe that we were not made to experience change as fast as we are forced to in this day and age. Inherent with change is *loss*. *Depression is a reaction to loss*. Change also causes stress. Some stress is good and healthy. However, too much change too fast causes unhealthy stress which leads to imbalance in our brain chemistry. This imbalance can lead to depression or bipolar depression. |
| **Fear** | We live in a society that sells expensive insurance policies after filling people with fear; fear of getting old, fear of getting sick, fear of losing the "things" we own, and fear of getting hurt. Most of the news that is on television and in the headlines of our newspapers is tragic and fear-producing. There is also the *fear* of nuclear annihilation or environmental disintegration.

Fear produces stress and thus imbalances our brain chemistry and may trigger depressive and manic-depressive mood swings. Intense fear can bring about immense stress and cause one's biochemistry to go wild! Often this enormous fear is related to an event that touches on a memory (conscious or subconscious) of a hurtful childhood experience. It may also have to do with touching on the memory of a trauma experienced as an adult. |

Fear (cont.)   Fear and dealing with fear, plays a major role in depression and manic depression (their causes and their relief). In addition to fears imposed by society, there are often many personal fears people struggle with. Some of these are: fear of survival—of not being able to make it in such a fast paced and heartless, at times even hostile world, fear of being rejected and fear of being alone or lonely. Another fear that many people wrestle with is the fear of being a *bad person,* since they were never told that they were good. Some were even told that they were no good as children. If each of us takes a courageous look at ourselves, we will learn what we fear. When we share our fears with another trustworthy person, we will see that those fears start to disappear. Deep and debilitating fears such as those involved in depression and bipolar depression are best looked into and healed with the help of a counselor. There are two excellent books on dealing with overcoming fear, the titles of which are listed in Appendix B.

> **As we share our fears with another trustworthy person, or even better, as we share our fears in a support group we will see those fears start to disappear!**

Choices   Having too many choices can lead to confusion, and we have so many choices today. Having many choices can be an advantage, but the more choices one has, the harder it is to make a decision and the longer the decision process takes.

Manipulation and Control	Many people are trying to manipulate us. Advertisers use our needs, wants, desires, interests, and weaknesses to sell us things. Companies spend *millions* of dollars on commercials. They use *powerful psychological techniques* to *ever so gently* bend and twist our minds, brainwashing us into believing we really need what they are trying to sell us. We would do well to seriously look at how this is affecting us. Rather than try to figure it out, just turn the TV off (especially advertisements). Then there are people who use *guilt* and similar methods to control us.
	We should be careful not to blame others too much, though. We do it too (often unconsciously). Does this manipulation and control affect us, especially *we* the sensitive-ones? You bet it does.
Busyness	The human body and spirit need rest, but we are so involved with our modern day god of busyness that we don't take time to rest anymore.
Oppression	Being in an oppressive environment where we are not allowed to express ourselves can lead to depression.

Oppression can lead to depression.

Sun	Not getting enough sun can contribute to depression. We must get a considerable amount of exposure to the sun to stay healthy. There is even a specific type of depression called *Seasonal Affective Disorder* or SAD. People who suffer from SAD get depressed specifically because of a lack of sunlight.
Joy	Does our lifestyle rob us of joy? Many people don't realize the joy they rob themselves of when they throw things away and buy new ones—instead of fixing the old ones. I feel so good when I fix something, or create something. Joy is the opposite of depression.

55

Instant Gratification

Aren't we robbing ourselves of the joy of anticipation? Doesn't it feel good to save for a new bicycle, clothes, a car or whatever? Doesn't immediate sex rob us of the joy and excitement of waiting? We also buy fast food instead of experiencing the joy of cooking. Credit cards epitomize our desire for instant gratification. Instead of saving with joy for what we want, we charge it, and get it immediately, only to find that we are behind bars till we pay for it. What are the bars? Can we see them? Can we see what is really binding us, oppressing us and depressing us?

Postpone gratification.

Practice patience and anticipation.

Anticipation makes life exciting!

Over Stimulation

There is too much stimulation in our society. We are constantly bombarded by stimuli. The mass media is one cause of this. People who live in large cities are often a victim of over stimulation. Human beings were not designed to endure constant stimulation. We need rest. We need a time of little or no stimulation to process information and rejuvenate ourselves. Constant stimulation is like a drug, eventually we become *numb* from it. We become insensitive to our environment, both physically and psychologically. We should rest and get away from the excessive stimulation on a regular basis. Try your bathtub. It's a great way to relax and limit sensory input.

Television

What do children spend the largest block of their waking hours doing? What is the easiest baby-sitter? *Who is really educating our children?* Unfortunately, the answer for many, is *television*. What is TV teaching our children (and ourselves as well), other than sensationalism, violence,

56

Television
(cont.)

immorality and spreading of fear? Sure there are good things on television, but how many of us are watching them? Sure, television is OK in moderation. But how many of us moderate? For many of us, television is consuming our lives! Instead of sharing our lives with one another, *instead of facing one another, we face the television.* Yet we wonder why we are so lonely and why we don't feel connected.

<u>**Television**</u>

Traffic

What frustration we often feel when in traffic! When I am on the highway, I often feel out of control. The driver behind me is following me too closely, but I can't tell him. If I can, I pull over and let him pass me. If I can't because there is another car next to me, I feel the mercury in my internal stress thermometer begin to rise.

Traffic lights are another source of this type of frustration. To deal with traffic problems in general, I once moved to a less congested area. It was much more relaxing to have this type of stress out of my life.

Value
Conflict

The following is an excerpt from my travel log as I was on extended personal travel observing other cultures:

Nov. 21, 1990
Gili Islands (Trawangen)
Indonesia

I look at the relatively simple people here, whose lives are uncluttered, compared to the lives of the people in the West, and I can't help but ask, Why? Why in the west, do we rush around like nuts all of the time, trying to get more things done in a day than we can comfortably do? Are these Indonesian people wrong? Are they not doing enough?

Or are we Westerners serving a 'god of busyness'? Has busyness become one of our modern day idols?

I know that for me, living in Western society is very unhealthy. The things that I value, society today does not seem to value very much. And society values things that, for me, have very little or no worth.

Some examples follow:

<u>Society's Values As I See Them:</u>

1. High emphasis on career, even to the extent of putting "it" before family and loved ones.

2. The importance of making a lot of money, and having a job with status.

3. It's O.K. for both parents to work and have someone else take care of the children.

4. Teachers get paid hardly enough to survive on, much less raise a family. Education is a low priority for our government when it comes to forking out the money.

5. Society does not value or reward the "creative" individual, but instead, it forces them into a mold. Businesses don't want to spend the money to create new things. They only see the short-term, quick buck. Change something a

little and sell it to someone else is the philosophy, instead of creating new things.

6. *Religion—*Science is the way and religion is of little or no value according to much of our society nowadays.

7. *Medicine—*Society wants private institutions and doctors. This deprives the poor and the middle class. Also, it reduces the productivity of the nation because people try to get a job with "good benefits" instead of a job they like the most and where they would be the most productive.

8. *Vacation—*Most U.S. businesses offer only 2 weeks a year.

9. The elderly are not valued much and are often hastily put into nursing homes.

10. Society values things, money, and leaving for better opportunity.

11. Speed. Getting things done in a hurry. Pushing others.

My Values (contrasted one for one with societal values)

1. I encourage a person to pursue what he or she is gifted at and what they like to do most. We will be the most happy and productive both as an individual and a nation if we do this.

2. Not placing such a high value on money. Money is needed to live, however, it is more important to have a job which you like and one that has "purpose," than to make lots of money at the expense of these.

3. I want myself and my wife to be the primary people rearing our children, not a stranger.

4. I value education and feel that we should pay our teachers well and investigate and improve the current stale methods of education.

5. Creativity is my life's blood. I must use my creative abilities. Our spirits need to create.

6. *God and faith are the basis for my life and actions.*

7. *Medicine—I would like to see socialized medicine. It would give more equality for all and would guarantee all people what I think is a basic human right. If a person is sick, he or she will receive medical attention no matter what his or her status is.*

8. *Vacation—People in England, Australia, New Zealand, and Europe have 4–6 weeks a year off. Why don't we? We think we produce more by this 2 week vacation life style. However, the extra time that we work is negated by the lack of efficiency in our "stale" workers. We are either stale or we get sick and take sick time. The end result is increased time off, less productive workers, and huge medical bills which could have been avoided. What do many of us need? More REST and relaxation!*

9. *I value senior citizens. I cherish them and listen to them. Within our "elderly" lie wisdom and experience.*

10. *Seek wisdom and values like humility, love, faithfulness, and sticking it out when times are rough.*

11. *I believe in accuracy, in doing things carefully and well. Let people take their time to do things well.*

> **These differences cause me great stress living in western society.**

The differences between the values society seems to encourage and our own personal values often cause great stress. It is important to hold on to values that are important to us and to seek out others who have similar values, so we feel validated and have a sense of belonging.

There are other theories concerning the causes of depression and bipolar depression. One of these is *Wolman's view of bipolar depression*:

Psychiatrist and author Benjamin Wolman believed manic depression is set up in our infancy by a mother who predominantly rejects her child. Then when she sees the child suffering, the mother (motivated by guilt) showers the child with affection. Wolman's view was found in the *International Encyclopedia of Psychiatry, Psychology, Psychoanalysis & Neurology*, p. 487.

Can you see how this cycle of *rejection, then showering with affection*, over and over again, could predispose a child to have bipolar depression? It seems so clear to me. When the child is rejected, he feels depressed. Then, from seemingly nowhere, the mother showers her child with affection, so the child gets elated. I once observed a mother treating an infant like this in public. The mother could not control herself. My heart and a prayer went out to that poor innocent child. It also went out to the mother, who was clearly in distress over her endlessly crying child and who clearly was not mature enough to be a mother.

It can easily be seen then, how a person could develop bipolar depression with this type of nurturing. One might ask, why doesn't a person with just plain depression swing to the other side? Such a person might not have been reared with both extremes—rejection and showering of affection. There may have been just an atmosphere of rejection or non-acceptance without the showering of affection. This atmosphere could predispose a person towards low self-esteem and unipolar depression.

I will mention again and again that it's not a blame game. I was sick and suffered because my parents were sick and suffered. My parents were sick and suffered because their parents were, and so on. The problem is a *multi-generational illness* or chain of unhealthy *learned* behaviors and thinking that must be broken or those behaviors and unhealthy thinking will continue down through the generations. It must be broken through the use of therapy, support groups, getting new information, grieving, and/or other methods of healing. We must face and understand what happened to us, or we will create a similar unhealthy atmosphere for our children, and perpetuate the disease.

Genes   Is it genes? Is bipolar behavior caused by genes and therefore hereditary? There are conflicting opinions and studies concerning this. Even the famous research study performed on the Amish people of Pennsylvania which supported the theory that bipolar depression is genetically inherited has been questioned for it's validity. I believe a person might have a genetic predisposition to a certain

61

Genes (cont.)   illness, but not that they are locked into being afflicted by it. Many an illness could be avoided simply by taking preventive measures. This includes illnesses thought to come from a genetic predisposition.

Location   Several of the pressures mentioned have to do with where we live. I was once in a high energy state and feeling afraid and a bit paranoid. In my work situation, I experienced a very oppressive atmosphere. When I spoke up for myself, the pressures only increased. I told the psychiatrist I was seeing at the time that I needed to get out of the situation or I would get depressed again. I wasn't sleeping well at night and had other symptoms of the manic phase of bipolar depression.

The doctor gave me a note that allowed me to take a sick leave. I immediately went to Martha's Vineyard. I felt safe there, and had no trouble sleeping through the night. The manic symptoms just disappeared! I felt good, peaceful, and not so afraid.

When I returned, I told this to the doctor and pointed out that the environment had so much to do with my cycles. He shrugged it off and said, "You can't just change where you live." I said, "You bet I can! It may be hard, but if that is an alternative to being medicated for the rest of my life you'd better believe I'll consider it." There is a wonderful insight to be learned here, namely that:

Bipolar (Manic) Depression is not only a chemical imbalance in the brain that can merely be treated with medication. It is clear that the chemical balance is affected by the environment in which we live.

The *environment* involves thoughts and feelings generated in response to our surroundings. Note that *environment* is both internal and external. The external environment is our surroundings. Our internal environment is the way we interpret things. A person with a weak internal environment might be more susceptible to variations or bombardments from his or her external environment. Healing and coping must address both internal and external environments. This is also documented under "Stress" in the "Self Pressures" section of this chapter.

Attachment is the cause of much suffering. I believe this statement is worth much thought. Depression has also been said to be a reaction to loss. I believe this is on the mark, and we should think deeply about the meaning of these statements. Attachment appears in many not so obvious forms. Some of them may be seemingly unrelated to our suffering. But upon careful inspection it is seen that some form of *attachment* and/or a *lack of love* is often at the root of our pain.

Hence, for healing we might learn how to *let go* and how to *love* properly. It is possible to form healthy attachments. In healthy attachments, we are gently attached. A gentle attachment is much easier to let go of. If we can not let go, or stubbornly hold on to something or someone, then we will experience pain and depression at their loss.

M. Scott Peck in *The Road Less Traveled* makes a brilliant observation when he says (on p133) "the attempt to avoid legitimate suffering lies at the root of all emotional illness." Could a lack of mental health be caused by an unwillingness to endure legitimate suffering? Here is an example of such: My girlfriend breaks up with me. I can't face and accept this loss, so I get depressed instead. A healthier response would be to grieve the loss and move on. This is sometimes more easily said than done, especially when grieving may not have been allowed by one's parents during childhood. Such a person isn't aware of the skills that are used in *letting go* of someone or something and grieving in a healthy way. If this is the case, these skills must be learned.

We must look very carefully to find the trigger or triggers of our depression. This takes careful self-observation and maybe with the help of a friend and/or a good therapist we will be able to learn what our triggers are. When we learn what the triggers of our depressions are, we can then find ways to avoid future depressions.

John Powell believes that a lack of love is the reason for our maladies. In his book titled, *The Secret of Staying in Love,* John Powell notes on p. 92: "The experimental evidence for the crippling effects of a loveless life is found in the office of every psychiatrist, filled with children and adults who have no awareness of their own worth, no sense of identity, who are filled with hatred and fear, and tortured by anxieties. Love is costly, but the alternatives are deadly." It is risky to love someone. It is risky to let someone love us, but as Powell says, the alternatives are deadly.

Is it a chemical imbalance in your brain?

The doctor says, "You have a chemical imbalance in your brain." That sounds scary, doesn't it? When this statement was made to me, I felt scared and possibly irreparable, or at least in need of brain surgery. Not all people react as such. Some people seem to be able to accept a statement like that easier than others. I was not one of them. I felt a strong need to question the validity and logic of what I had been told.

When I asked my doctor, "What is wrong with me?" he said, "You have a chemical imbalance in your brain." But he did no blood tests! I asked, "What causes it?" He said, "I don't know, but lithium will bring the balance back." I asked, "How does lithium work?" He said, "We don't know." I thought, "This doesn't make much sense. Here is a doctor who is treating me for an illness and he doesn't know what causes it. He says I have a chemical imbalance in my brain, but doesn't do any tests to prove it, and he doesn't know how the pill works that he wants me to take to deal with it." He says, "It just works." I say, there is too much *faith* here in guess work. I don't want to be treated for an illness that no one understands, with a pill that no one understands how it works. Some science that is! Read *Toxic Psychiatry* listed in Appendix B for facts on the flaws in the genetic and biochemical theories.

I would also like to note here that these are only some of the doctors I have seen. There are also more capable, less medication-pushy doctors out there who operate with a whole-person approach and do their job well. People with severe depression or bipolar may require medication—at least for a while. However, the most effective doctors also encourage using many other tools as well. When a person is depressed, it is hard to distinguish the more effective doctors from the less effective ones. It could be quite helpful if a trusted relative or friend helped the depressed person or bipolar sufferer choose the psychiatrist or therapist.

Lithium is usually the prescribed medicine for people who suffer from bipolar depression. Research has found that only 1/3 of the patients suffering from bipolar depression who were treated with lithium, achieved long term stability. The other 2/3 were revisited with highs and lows. Hence, lithium is not the cure-all that it once was expected to be. Accordingly, we must use other means to get and stay well.

Lithium also has side-effects. These can be found in any Physicians Desk Reference (PDR). Side-effects include: hand tremors, possible death if overdosed, dryness of the mouth, weight gain, and diminished creativity. See the PDR for the rest.

As an engineer and counselor who knows something about the brain, I must agree that in the body and brain there are multiple chemical reactions and chemical balances occurring at every moment of our lives. Neurotransmitters and other functions of the brain are related to depression and bipolar depression. Statistics show that antidepressants and lithium are often effective to a degree. Thus, I believe that depression is linked to a chemical imbalance in the brain.

<u>Some questions I have are:</u>

1. Does a chemical imbalance cause depression, or does depression cause a chemical imbalance?

2. If a chemical imbalance causes depression, then what might be the cause of the chemical imbalance?

In the middle ages, people were healed by ministering to the whole person. A person's spiritual condition was believed to affect their body. Since the discovery of chemical effects on the brain, including antidepressants and lithium, and with genetic factors being unveiled, it seems that psychiatrists too often push the psychological and spiritual elements aside, in favor of a solely medication oriented approach to treatment.

What the medication treatment approach misses is the fact that there are switches in our brain which cause our brain to secrete chemicals. These switches, if not operating properly, may cause a chemical imbalance in the brain, resulting in depression. However, if the switches are operating properly, they will cause a proper chemical balance, a healthy state of mind and physical well-being.

This concept is brought out in and woven all through Shad Helmstetter's book, *What To Say When You Talk To Yourself.* Further evidence substantiating the *thought-switch* theory is the success of *cognitive therapy.* Cognitive therapy is based on the theory that people's emotions are controlled by their views and opinions of the world. *Depression results when patients constantly put themselves down, expect to fail, make inaccurate assumptions of what others think of them, and have a negative attitude toward the world and the future.* The therapist uses various techniques of talk therapy to alleviate the negative thought patterns and negative beliefs. The therapist challenges our harmful thoughts and ways of looking at things.

Cognitive therapy has been as successful as antidepressants in relieving depression. I believe, and have experienced, that the recurrence of depression and its severity is much less after the cognitive approach has been used because it gets closer to the root of the problem. Medications treat the symptoms of the problem, rather than the cause. Often, when the use of antidepressants is discontinued, depression will recur in time. Hence, a person may take antidepressants again and thus the person may become chemically dependent or psychologically dependent—creating another problem.

If the theory of the *thought switch* is correct, then when we *think healthy thoughts,* our brain chemistry will naturally balance itself as it does in a healthy person. The depression will most likely not recur, as long as we keep thinking healthy thoughts and living a healthy, balanced life.

Here are some examples of how powerfully thoughts can affect our bodies:

1. The old saying "You make me sick to my stomach."
2. Once I was so angry at my sister, instead of expressing the anger or telling her how I felt she wronged me, I held it in. This unexpressed anger gave me a terrible backache that caused me to stop dead in my tracks. I literally couldn't move until I said a prayer for my sister, attempting to forgive her. This helped me to release the anger and I could walk again.

66

3. Ulcers are often attributed to worriers.
4. Asthma sufferers are often people who repress rage.
5. There is the simple but vivid example of a person who feels embarrassed and turns red in the face.

If thoughts are this powerful in causing the secretion of chemicals in our bodies and causing muscles to constrict, giving us great pain and affecting how we feel, what might negative thoughts be doing to our brains and the chemicals it secretes?

Other proofs of the success of the *thought* approach are: the great numbers of psychologically hurting people who have been healed in groups such as Alcoholics Anonymous, Codependents Anonymous, ACOA (adult children of alcoholics) Depressive and Manic Depressive support groups and other support groups and church groups, not to mention the one-on-one relationships of friend-to-friend, parent-to-son, husband-to-wife that have been so healing.

> **One reason so many people get stuck in** ***believing that only medication can help them*** ***get well*** **is that the people healed in the groups mentioned above seldom make it into the cure rate surveys, nor are they aired on the nightly news.**

New drugs make it into the news. Genetic links make it into the news. *Electro-convulsive shock therapy* makes it into the news. How Lithium saved the life of an actress, makes it into the news. Why not mention natural methods of healing, humane methods of healing?

Another reason people get stuck in the drug trap is that we are an impatient society. We want fast food. We want fast cars. We want quick money and *we want fast cures.* Pills *seem* to provide this. People take pills and they survive. They cope, but they do not live fully.

67

Some things in life take time. When will we realize this? When will we realize that we are a restless society? We must slow down and give ourselves the time and the methods that we need in order to heal.

Most people in the previously mentioned *support groups* do not use drugs. The following are some of the *healing elements* I've observed in support groups:

1. They allow people to express their thoughts and feelings without being judged (*acceptance*). It seems to me, from hearing many people speak in these groups, that our society doesn't accept or allow people to say what they really think and feel. There are set, acceptable norms. If we don't fit in, or play the roles, we are considered weird and are ostracized. As one man put it at a support group, "This is the only place that I can really say how I feel." My first thought was, "How sad." My next thought was, "How true." And then I thought, "What a sad society we live in." Too often, this *disallowing of people to express their thoughts and feelings* is also practiced in our families, with our friends, and our closest relatives. Thank God for support groups.

2. Support groups help people become *aware* of themselves, of their feelings, and of why they behave the way they do.

3. People in support groups become aware of unhealthy ways they may be relating; they also become aware of their thinking process and learn which thinking patterns are unhealthy. From other's sharing, the members also learn *healthy ways of thinking, relating, and behaving.*

4. Support groups teach members how to *listen*.

5. People in support groups learn to accept and understand their feelings of hurt, anger, hate, sadness, and frustration as well as feelings of happiness, joy, and peace. They help people develop skills to express these intense feelings in healthy, acceptable ways.

> **Negative thoughts often lead to more negative thoughts which can cause our brain chemistry to become imbalanced.**

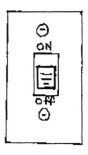

Thought switch

Remember who has the power to flip it.
Don't give that power away!

Why not assume a whole-person approach to healing and be open to using a variety of methods? One may use all or several of the following: the Family Systems Theory approach, the psychosomatic approach, the cognitive/behavioral approach, support groups, inner child work, meditation, spirituality, exercise, diet, sleep tinkering, the psychoanalytical approach, the biochemical approach, the genetic approach and all of the other approaches mentioned in this book. Use whatever works and has the fewest side-effects. Put each in its proper place however, by evaluating the pros and cons of the various methods. Let us not be so quick to discard one in favor of the other.

The approaches to wellness mentioned above, as well as numerous others will be described further in the next chapter and the remainder of this book.

Chapter 4

TOOLS

for the Depressed Person

and

the Person Who Is Hyper or High

The first and most important thing to realize in overcoming depression and bipolar depression is that it takes hard work and a dedicated commitment to health. It requires a commitment to work at becoming healthy *all of the time,* when we feel poorly and even—and especially—*when we feel good.* Maintenance work will keep one from getting depressed again. It may be tough at times to discipline ourselves, however, much of the work is fun. It's about being good to ourselves and taking care of ourselves, and that feels good. It feels good to be in control again, to realize we have the power to influence our mood swings and emotions without the use of drugs (or for some, with less medication). What a joy!

There are tapes in our brain that were written, to a large degree, by our parents, when we were children. They were also written by other parts of our environment, like our education, friends, society, and by *our choices.* The tapes of a person who gets depressed must regularly be rewritten to some degree. The tapes that I am referring to are tapes of negativity and pessimism, for example: "You will never amount to anything," "You are careless," "You mental retard." Some people may have been in an entirely *corrosive environment,* such as a person who had a critical parent that rarely praised and encouraged them, but who instead, relentlessly badgered them with constant criticism. A sad thing about such a scenario, is that a person who has experienced that kind of abuse often doesn't even know it is abuse because it is all they knew. To them, *such behavior is normal!* Hence, he or she will try to *love* other people in a similarly abusive way.

Healthy people won't stand for abusive treatment. Thus, when picking friends or a mate, an abused person *who hasn't gotten counseling* will either experience continual rejection from healthy people or will pick a partner who thinks this *impostor of love* is love also. In the latter case, the disease is just perpetuated.

In a way, *depression,* bipolar depression, and many other so-called mental illnesses may be considered as *opportunity*. They awaken us. They call us to growth, to get out of this vicious cycle and enter into a fuller, happier life.

The destructive tapes can be rewritten. They can be replaced through counseling and through the hard work of self-monitoring and correcting known, unhealthy thought patterns such as negative and critical thinking. We must replace these tapes with healthy thoughts which include warm, positive affirmations such as:

- I am full of love, light, peace, and joy.
- I am OK.
- I am a unique and valuable human being.
- I am special, even if someone else may think I am not.
- I don't need to be loved—not if it's at the cost of myself.
- I deserve to be treated with respect.
- I don't need to dwell on negative thoughts that make me feel unhappy.
- I choose to think happy, peaceful thoughts that bring me peace.
- I am whole.
- I am complete.

There are so many more affirmations. Attend an Adult Children of Alcoholics (ACOA), Codependents Anonymous (CODA), or Al-Anon meeting and you will find lists full of warm affirmations to build yourself up. You will also find people who will affirm you and build you up. You can make up your own list of affirmations. Our own affirmations are the most powerful because only we know exactly what we need to hear.

There are many healthy tapes or memories that have been given to us by our parents: those of love (real love) and encouragement, and those of praise and healthy nurturing. We might remember to be thankful to our parents for these and spend some time repeating them to ourselves. But along with those good memories, we must have the courage to look at the ones that did (and do) cause us pain. It is a matter of sorting out. Let us separate the healthy nurturing from the unhealthy. Let us be thankful for the healthy nurturing while healing the unhealthy. Let us "separate the wheat from the chaff" and burn the chaff while saving the wheat.

A very powerful tool for the healing of bipolar depression is realizing that *the higher we get, the lower we will go* and the lower we go, the higher we will get. It is like the pendulum example; the further the pendulum goes on the *up-side*, the further it will swing on the *down* side. This awareness has helped me to let go of the excessive euphoric feelings I have had in the past and the mild ones I still get once in a while. Euphoric feelings are hard to let go of, because they feel good. But depression feels so terribly bad that if I can lessen those feelings by letting go of the euphoria, it seems like a worthwhile trade. In accord with this, meditation, or doing calming things when feeling euphoric, helps create the balance needed. The reward has been quite worth the sacrifice.

> ### *The higher we get, the lower we will go.*

Questions

Depression and bipolar depression are often cyclical in nature. They often repeat at the same time of year, or in response to the same kind of triggering event. Some questions I have asked myself to help find what might trigger my own depressions and *what might be a key to healing are:*

A.   After my first serious clinical depression, was there ever a time, was there ever a year that I went through without getting depressed or high?

B.   If there was such a time, why didn't I get depressed then, or high then?

C.   What was my life situation like during that period?

D.   What was going on in me and around me at that time?

E.   When was the next time I got depressed (or high)? Why?

73

These questions were immensely helpful to me. I found that (after the initial onslaught of my cycling) I did have years in which I didn't get manic or depressed. During these times, I was going out with a girl who I felt *loved* me. Hence, I went on a quest to learn what love is and to learn how to give love and receive love. My journey has also led me to discover *what love is not*. I have learned that there are many things disguised as love, which in fact are not love at all! Beware of the counterfeits!

Another thing I found was that *I needed to learn how to love and esteem myself*. This lesson was learned the hard way, after I came crashing down when a love relationship ended. I became depressed each time the one I made my false god or *love source* (in my case, a woman) went away.

Now my esteem, my love, comes from God in Heaven. God never goes away. Sometimes it seems He does, but I find out later that it was me who was absent, not God. God never abandons us. Now I esteem myself through prayer. Or rather, I let God esteem me. I'm also esteemed by healthy, caring and affirming friends, family, support groups and a men's group at church. These are much less vulnerable, much more stable sources than just one woman.

Depression and manic depression are stubborn illnesses. They don't go away easily. To deal with my depression and bipolar depression, I used a *multifaceted* approach to healing. Moving depression or manic depression away is like pushing a car that is out of gas. If one person alone tries to push the car, he will probably fail. If however, 5 or 6 people push the car, it will move! It is similar with depression and manic depression. One strategy alone is usually not sufficient to facilitate healing and maintain mood stability. However, using a multifaceted approach, the depression or manic depression, like the car, will be moved away!

The following is a list of practical tools that can be helpful in overcoming depression. Some of these tools though briefly stated, are quite effective. Don't underestimate their healing power. The list is very long. Probably no one will use all of them. They are simply a selection of tools. You be the mechanic. Pick the ones you need and go to work. Good luck!

Tools For The Depressed Person

1)   DON'T ISOLATE

Don't spend too much time alone. Force yourself to get out and be with people. It is said that, "an idle mind is the workshop of the devil." Too much time alone can lead a person to despair. Get with people who understand you. Support groups are excellent for this purpose. Spend time with a friend, with someone you know who cares about you. Remember though, no one person can be everything for you. We need many people to satisfy our needs and to heal, especially if we are in a place of great pain.

2)   SUPPORT GROUPS

It is helpful to be with people who understand us. We feel so alone when no one understands us. There are many existing support groups where we can meet people who understand how we feel. This will help to dissipate that terrible feeling of being the only one who feels like we do. Create a support network of friends. Spend time with people who share your dreams, goals, philosophy, hobbies, morals, etc. I have found twelve-step support groups to be the most effective of the support groups that I have attended. They are based on the original 12 step program developed by Bill Wilson and Dr. Bob who founded the now well known Alcoholics Anonymous (AA) support groups in 1935.

Other 12 step groups have modified the steps slightly to address the specific problems they deal with. I have found Codependents Anonymous (CODA) to be the most accepting, nurturing, freeing, and safe environment in which to heal and get information about what it means to be healthy. CODA is a 12 step group. Normally 12 step groups don't cost anything except for a voluntary contribution (people usually give $1 each.) To locate a support group in your area, try the phone numbers in Appendix A. The following is an excellent resource to help find or create a support group:

The Self Help Sourcebook: Finding and Forming Mutual Aid Self-Help Groups. 5th ed. Self Help Clearinghouse, Denville, NJ 07834 1995.

If you can't find a support group in your area, you can start one. Churches and hospitals are usually willing to provide a room. Then just run an add in the newspaper to inform anyone interested of the time, place, and purpose of the meeting. A basic rule that I recommend the group should have is: No one is to interrupt while another person is sharing. Another one is: no one should offer advice without first asking the person if they want it. It would be very helpful to obtain a *Suggested Rules and Guidelines for CODA Meetings* package and model your group after that. See Appendix A for sources of 12 Step CODA information.

3)   THERAPY

Get into therapy with a good therapist. People who seek therapy should be congratulated; it takes a lot of courage. For those who are not interested in the drug solution alone, research has found that Cognitive/Behavioral Therapy and Interpersonal Therapy are as successful in treating depression as drug therapy.

In therapy, one can do a tremendous amount of growing that people who don't attend therapy may never do. These changes can bring about a deeper appreciation of life. They can also build us up and give us the strength that will take us through the storms to the rainbows that await us on the other side.

Cognitive Therapy

Cognitive therapy challenges negative, over-critical, and other unhealthy ways of thinking that can lead to and perpetuate depression and bipolar depression. Most often we are not aware of our negative thinking and that it is causing us to get depressed. The therapist is trained to look for unhealthy ways of thinking such as: overly self-critical thinking, irrational thinking, worrying, all-or-nothing thinking, perfectionistic thinking, inappropriate feelings of guilt, and others.

The therapist may then offer us other healthier ways of thinking. He or she may teach us how to catch our internal critic and disarm it. Then we must substitute the healthier ways of thinking. If we have grown up with a parent who controlled and manipulated us with guilt, a guilt ridden conscience is in place. Hence we learn to question and re-write our own consciences.

Family Counseling

Family counseling can also be effective because a counselor who offers marriage and family counseling should know *family systems theory*. The therapist will be able to map out a family tree and see how unhealthy thought patterns have been transmitted down the generations. If the whole family (or as many members as possible) attends counseling together, the therapist can observe any unhealthy ways that the family members use to

76

relate. Dysfunctional ways of relating often contribute to depression and bipolar. Group counseling can be used to *mimic* family if they're unavailable.

Suggestions for seeking a therapist:

A.   Interview therapists until you find one you feel comfortable and safe with.

B.   Check credentials. Do they have a degree such as an MA, MSW or Ph.D. in the field of counseling or psychotherapy? Are they licensed? There are several licensing agencies. An example is: "Licensed Professional Counselor (LPC)." Are they a member of the "American Counseling Association," "American Association for Marital and Family Counseling," or any other professional counseling associations?

C.   Choose a therapist who is familiar with the concept of boundaries. Learning what boundaries are and how to set healthy boundaries is a crucial step in healing.

D.   A good choice might be someone who knows and uses counseling approaches such as: Cognitive therapy, Interpersonal therapy, Cognitive/Behavioral therapy, or Family Systems therapy.

E.   Use a therapist who is knowledgeable about, understands, and uses codependence treatment methods. The core symptom of a problem with codependence is low self-esteem. Low self-esteem often fuels depression and bipolar disorder.

F.   Choose a therapist who knows how to treat stress disorders. High stress is the number one trigger for depression and bipolar depression. Ask the therapist if they know how to use *systematic desensitization* which is an effective tool to deal with stress. There are other methods also. Be sure your therapist teaches you stress reduction techniques.

G.   Inner child work therapy is also very powerful in healing. This deals with healing childhood hurts. Unresolved childhood hurt, I believe, is the origin of most mental illness.

H.   I also believe in selecting a therapist who listens, but will also answer questions if asked. Choose one who will guide you to find your own answers, but will also share information you may need to learn to help your healing process. I don't like just talking. I desire feedback such as: insights, helpful advice and instruction from a counselor.

I.   If there is an alcohol or substance abuse problem in the family, the therapist should be familiar with alcoholism, substance abuse and how they affect those in the family who are non-users.

J.   If you don't believe in taking medication, make sure the therapist doesn't either. My experience has been that psychiatrists usually advocate the drug approach and are very expensive. Social workers and therapists with counseling degrees are generally cheaper and often use talk therapy rather than drugs. Some believe in using both.

K.   Find someone with a belief system similar to your own. You may want someone of the same religion or who shares some important values you have.
• Does the therapist share your belief in using medication or not?
• Does the therapist believe in a whole-person approach?
• Make your own list of questions about what is important to you.

L.   I also recommend that you seek someone who you feel is a compassionate and caring person. I don't think therapy works very well without these qualities.

M.   What is the therapist's own experience in hurting? Is he or she in a recovery program? Which one? Is he or she healed enough to share some of his or her story? They should be able to.

N.   Choose a therapist who advocates 12 step programs and self-help. Also one who is able to do *group counseling*—which can be *very* effective in overcoming depression and bipolar disorder.

O.   Ask if the therapist will accept insurance payments, as well as how much it will cost. Ask what you will be getting for your money and what is the length of each therapy session. Be sure to settle this before beginning therapy.

P.   Ask friends for their recommendations. See if your job provides referrals, or call the psychology or counseling department at a nearby university. Someone at your church or other place of worship may offer direction. There is always the yellow pages if one has no success with the previous suggestions. There is no reason not to use the Yellow Pages if you interview the therapist thoroughly.

Q.   The best way to start the interview is to ask the therapist what treatment methods they specialize in and what other tools they use. Do this before you tell them what you want. Otherwise they may tailor their answers to your needs. These questions must be asked before entering therapy. Once therapy has begun, the therapist will most likely not answer many of these questions.

R.   Please remember that the therapist is a person too. He or she will probably find your questions intimidating. However, *the client has every right to carefully interview a therapist with whom he or she will trust his or her mind.* Much will be learned about the therapist and their abilities during the interviewing process. Much time and money can be saved by a thorough interviewing process. If a therapist refuses to be interviewed, or you don't feel good about the person, don't use him or her!

S.   Remember that no therapist will satisfy all of the criteria above. Prioritize your questions and choose a therapist who offers what is most important to you.

4)   HUMILITY

Humility is probably the single most essential element in the healing process. Often the people who don't heal are those who are too proud to admit that something is wrong and that they need help. Some parents have the attitude, "my kid isn't going to see a therapist; there is nothing wrong with him!" Individuals often have a similar attitude, "I'm fine, I don't need any help!" Meanwhile, the person's life is in shambles. It is sad, but in many cases, the person must hit rock bottom and be desperate before he or she seeks help. When we admit we need help, that we can not do it alone, we are opening a door. A door to healing. Inside the door we find that there are many people who are willing to help and a God who is willing to help. Let's open the door.

> **Humility is probably the single most essential element in the healing process.**

79

5)   HEALTHY THINKING

Healthy thinking includes forgiveness, love, and caring. I have found that my depression and euphoria were directly related to the way I was thinking. I grew up with an extremely critical father, and learned to think critically about myself and others. I have thousands of hours of critical parental tapes in my brain. As I became aware of my thought patterns, I noticed that I'd get angry at someone for something he did that hurt me. Then I would think of another person and what they did which hurt me. And on and on. *If there was a huge white board with one minute black speck on it, I would focus on the speck.*

Oh, if I only knew of the toxins that I was dumping into my system by this kind of thinking. If I only knew how out of whack I was making my brain chemistry. My thinking spiraled downward. Of course my critic certainly did not spare me from its scrutiny, from its tunnel vision, which only would see negative things in myself as well as in other people. "Judge and you will be judged." "Forgive and you will be forgiven." How true those words are! I had to learn how to catch my critical thoughts and stop them. I had to learn how to forgive! I had to learn how to forgive and how to be less critical of others and of myself. That was, and still is hard work. Though it is much easier now, reaping the rewards of peace of mind, stable emotions, and no huge mood swings is certainly worth the work.

Forgiveness

Forgiveness is an ongoing "process"
(not just a quick "I forgive you")
it takes effort & work

Just as a wound takes dressing
care and time
to heal
so does forgiveness

Usually prayer for the offender
is the best dressing for psychological hurt

Imagine taking anger or hate and turning it into a prayer—**how difficult**! But it is so healing. I testify to you that forgiveness works, since so much of my healing has come from the simple, yet difficult decision to

80

forgive. Forgiveness and prayer not only stop toxic chemicals from being dumped into our systems, but begins re-balancing our out of whack brain chemistry.

Although we must forgive in order to heal, we must also protect ourselves. If someone is constantly doing hurtful things to us and we are forgiving them and not challenging their behavior, we hurt ourselves and we do them an injustice as well. We must learn to set boundaries to protect what we treasure. We must communicate to others what is important to us and enforce boundaries (which protect what is important to us) with *consequences* for hurtful behavior. There will be more about boundaries later on in this chapter.

6)   PIECES OF THE PUZZLE

Often there is no simple, all inclusive answer to a problem. It is like putting together a puzzle. The pieces come one at a time. We must always be looking, so as not to miss one. All of our puzzles have some different pieces, some are common, some are unique.

7)   LEADING A BALANCED LIFE

As human beings, we have many needs we must satisfy in order to stay healthy (see chapter on HUMAN NEEDS). Can you imagine what a person would look like if he or she always read or watched TV in their spare time and never exercised? One does not have to imagine too hard, we just need to take a look around us. There are so many who have bought into a sedentary life. Can you imagine what a person would be like who always worked and never vacationed or rested or had fun? Yet isn't that like many of us? We need balance between work, play and rest. We need to have a balance between intellectual pursuits and socializing. We need balance between time with others and time alone, time in spiritual pursuits and time performing worldly tasks.

8)   SLOW DOWN!

Our society is moving so swiftly that many of its members are experiencing tremendous stress. Remember we have a choice. We don't have to join in. We can choose to have more rest and enjoyment in our lives. There is an answer to the madness.

9)   FOCUS

This is another answer and coping mechanism. Figure out what the most important things in your life are and focus on them.

Light a candle in your room. Sit with the candle in silence. The simplicity of a single slowly burning candle helps one learn how to focus and relax.

10)   MEDICATION

Take medication, if necessary, but use other means to combat depression as well. A pill alone will not solve the problem. Take all medication under the supervision of a psychiatrist. If you feel really low and can't seem to get out of your depression, you may in fact need an anti-depressant. They can be helpful to those who have a real need for them. However, one should never take medication for a psychologically related problem without being in therapy also.

The preference of some people is to accomplish emotional healing, put support systems in place and then gradually *reduce* and/*or stop* their medication with the supervision of a psychiatrist. Other more severe and persistent cases may need ongoing medication. Those who choose to stop medication ought to be careful when doing so. Sometimes one may experience a strong withdrawal reaction when ceasing medication abruptly. It could even cause a relapse into depression or bipolar. Such a reaction may be caused by either a physical or psychological dependence that has developed on the medication. Usually when stopping medication, it is tapered off by using lower and lower doses. Again, seek the advice of your psychiatrist if you desire to change medication doses or stop it altogether. See Appendix B for a book on how to stop psychiatric medications by Dr. Peter Breggin.

When medication is administered properly and responsibly, it can be a wonderful gift and can jump-start the healing process for someone who is deeply depressed or in a euphoric state. However, medication is sometimes handed out too easily and without proper discretion. Numerous people are being given too much medication. Often people need to be in therapy working through their problems but instead they are only given the quick and easy fix—a pill. Sadly, giving pills is quite *profitable* when compared with therapy. Consequently, insurance companies and HMO's often require it. Many psychiatrists have also seen the financial returns that medication affords them as opposed to therapy.

Sometimes taking medication cheats us out of living fully, and learning what we need to learn to stop the pain of depression and bipolar. A favorite example I like to use is the following:

Imagine you put your hand on a hot stove. Your hand is beginning to burn. To stop the pain, would you stick a needle full of Novocain into your hand and leave it on the burner? Or would you learn what the pain is trying to teach you? Namely, to take your hand off of the scorching stove and never put it on there again!

Similarly, many psychiatrists and doctors dole out powerful psychiatric medications that dull the symptoms instead of helping their patients heal the root causes that brought them their pain in the first place. Sadly, too often the symptoms are treated in lieu of the causes that need to be resolved. The hand continues to burn, but you don't even know it because it is so sedated.

Often medicine is needed to ease the pain or moderate moodswings when either is severe. However, be sure that you are also learning to take your hand off the hot stove by receiving good therapy and using all other tools available to you as well.

11)   HARD PHYSICAL WORK

Sweat-producing physical work is healthy. A hike in the woods is so refreshing to our body and our mind. Exercise, jogging, basketball and aerobics are good, too. Some years ago while visiting Nepal, I started to get depressed. I decided to go for a trek in the Himalayan mountains. It was a grueling, sweat-producing climb. My depression quickly lifted as the grueling climb brought me into the present moment. I believe depression has a lot to do with wrong thinking, worrying, and not being in the present. (If the present isn't exactly wonderful, then work to change it.) During the hike there was no time for worrying. I was too concerned about how I was going to make the next step and too enveloped by the breathtaking scenery to stay depressed for long.

12)   SLEEP TINKERING

Changing sleep patterns can have an antidepressant effect.

83

During times in my life when I am under a lot of stress, my sleep patterns change. It almost seems as though this is a *survival mechanism* to get me out of the stress that I am in. For example, during the daytime hours is when I am experiencing the excessive daily stress. It may be job stress, or the stress that can come from living with an uncooperative or extremely controlling partner. If I am awake at night when all others are sleeping, then "I am free" and not "controlled" by the stresses that take place during the day. Hence, I feel less depressed.

It can easily be seen that if I have "responsibilities" during the day, changing sleep patterns and being awake much of the night could be a problem. I use the following approach.

If I am not sleeping through the night:

A. I don't worry about it. Worry intensifies the problem.

B. I go with the flow and use the time to pray, write or do whatever I like.

C. Knowing that I must get sleep, I adjust my sleeping pattern by getting to bed much earlier. If I am waking at 4 A.M. instead of 6 A.M. I'll go to bed at 8 P.M., instead of 10 P.M. It works! This puts me more in tune with my biological clock (what my body wants) at this particular time in my life. It puts me more in control of my life (I do what I want at 4 A.M.). It takes me out of the stress of being at the demands of others, at least partially. It gives me the "free" time to myself that I need so much. I also fulfill my sleep needs by going out to my car at lunch time and taking a nap. This often makes the difference between a day of drudgery and a happy day for me (and those around me). I feel so much better when I get the sleep that I need. I ignore the so called accepted rules of when we are "supposed to sleep" and sleep when I need to. This will not solve all the problems. The source of stress must be dealt with. But it is a great "tool" for coping. If it works, use it. It does for me! So I use it.

If a person isn't having difficulties sleeping, it is usually best to maintain a regular sleep pattern. Going to sleep at the same time every night and getting up the same time helps one to develop a regular sleep pattern. Staying up late at night and not getting enough sleep can contribute to burnout and depression. Regular and sufficient sleep help to avoid stress and depression.

If a person is sleeping too much when they are depressed, cutting their sleep time shorter by getting up earlier can sometimes have an antidepressant effect.

13)   SIMPLE CREATIVE TASKS

Produce beautiful things which can be seen. Plant flowers. Make a belt. Engage in some kind of craft. These things are *spirit feeding, life giving activities*. There are many books in the library concerning the different types of crafts available.

14)   TUNE IN

To get and stay healthy we must tune in to what our individual needs are. We must tune in to "how we are feeling" and what the circumstances are at the time we are feeling what we are feeling. It has taken quite a while for me to become aware of what causes my stress. It seems that people get so used to having stress all of the time and get beyond the point where they even realize what is causing the stress. Then an illness sets in, either physical sickness or emotional sickness, and we are baffled as to the reason why. It is necessary to allow ourselves a regular time of quiet and rest in order to learn to recognize what we are feeling. On the contrary, being busy all of the time and always stimulated, we are often too *distracted* to tune in to our sources of stress.

15)   NATURE

Nature calms the mind and fills the spirit. Take a walk in the woods or park. Nature is a source of life. When we spend time out in nature, we get filled with the beauty of creation. Our bodies and minds tend to *take on* our surroundings, whatever they are. Would you rather take on the buzz of a busy and hectic city, or the serenity of a beautiful sunset? Maybe a balance of the two would be good. However, many of us are constantly in the busy city (or general hectic-ness of life). Remember, take time to smell the roses!

16)   MEDITATION

Take time for meditation, prayer, or at least a quiet time. Reserve some time during the day to just sit and relax, with little or no stimulation. If you have trouble releasing the stress from your mind and body, try listening to a guided relaxation tape. These are available from book stores and health food stores. Such relaxation time gives the body and brain a chance to replenish chemicals used in dealing with stress. These chemicals are depleted by the endless stimulation and demands which are put on us during a typical day in modern society. It is when these chemicals are used up that stress begins to take its toll on us, leading to physical or mental breakdown. We *must* give our bodies and our brains the time to replenish these chemicals. In our fast paced society, sleep alone is often not enough to restore our anti-stress chemical reserves. We must engage in things that are relaxing or un-stress-producing. Such things include: meditation, prayer, listening to a favorite album, knitting, crocheting, playing sports, lying on the beach, photography, art, writing, woodworking. Engage in any *simple physical activity* —preferably a creative one— that is relaxing. If you use your imagination, you will discover that there are many more.

To meditate:

1. Find a quiet place.
2. Get in a relaxed position, either lying down or sitting.
3. Close your eyes, but do not go to sleep.
4. Put everything else out of your mind. During this time, pretend nothing else matters.
5. Repeat a word or phrase over and over in your mind.
6. Perform your meditation for at least ten minutes at a time.

Doing this type of meditation for ten minutes or more per day helps one relax and causes one's anti-stress chemicals to be replenished. It should also translate into better health and an increased sense of well-being. One caution: Be sure the word or phase which you choose to repeat over and over is healthy and wholesome, or at least neutral. Healthy and wholesome might be a word or scripture from the Bible, or the word "love." Neutral would be a word such as "today." Another would be a phrase like " I am confident."

17)   LET GO

Learn to *let go* of things, attitudes, and people. There are many attitudes we have that cause us pain. Often the unwillingness to let go of a person or thing causes us pain. This includes relinquishing inordinate desires. For instance, a man might feel attracted to a woman and desire to have a relationship with her. She, however, is not interested. Instead of moving on, he continually wishes that he could have her and whenever he sees her he continues in his desire for her. This unhealthy thinking can happen toward a person or a thing. If continued, this thinking develops anger, jealousy, and a host of other painful emotions which can lead us to depression. We must release that which we cannot have. We must abandon inordinate desires if we want to heal. There are many more, including inappropriate sexual desires.

Some examples of this are: a man desiring another man's wife or a woman desiring another woman's husband. Fleeting thoughts are normal, however nurturing such thoughts by dwelling on them is unhealthy and can lead one to depression.

18)   LOOK FOR THE GOOD IN A SITUATION

Many good things can come out of a seemingly bad situation if we look for them. For example, when my girlfriend was leaving me, I started to get afraid and to feel depressed. Then I said to myself, "No, I will not get depressed. What *good* can come out of this?" I began to see many good things that I could do with my new-found time: I could spend more time with friends; I could see my grandfather; I could write the book you are now reading. So potential tragedy was turned to joy and some good works, instead of depression.

19)   HOBBIES

It brings much joy to us to make something—to create something. Often, time we spend worrying or thinking negatively could be better spent on a hobby or craft we enjoy. In this society, where we have machines that do everything for us, we are missing *the joy of doing things with our hands*. Hobbies are *sources of life*. Instead of watching TV one night, try working on a hobby you like and see the joy and energy it brings you.

20)   EXERCISE

Go to a gym or to the park at least once a week (preferably 3 times a week) and exercise a little. Better yet, exercise till you sweat and for about 20 minutes at a time. Bike, hike, whatever you like. Studies have clearly demonstrated the anti-depressive effects of exercise. People who are the most depressed before exercising show the greatest improvement in how they feel after exercising.

21)   SPEND TIME WITH PEOPLE WHO ARE HEALTHY

Spend time with people who have healthy attitudes and healthy thinking. We truly do become like those we spend time with. So if we want to be healthy, we had better spend time with healthy people.

22)   GET INVOLVED IN A SOCIAL PROJECT, A CAUSE

Get involved in something bigger than yourself: feeding the hungry, helping the homeless, attending peace demonstrations, working to save the environment, etc. Being involved in a *cause* helps us forget ourselves and accomplish something good at the same time.

23)   SIMPLE PHYSICAL ACTIVITY

Engage in a simple physical activity daily. A woman at a stress seminar I attended told us that a study was done on people who lived to be over 100 years old. The answer to their longevity was neither diet, nor climate. The two things that were found in common in all of these peoples' lives were:

> 1. They felt part of a *community* (wanted, needed, loved and supported)
> 2. They each performed a simple physical task every day. Knitting, crocheting, pottery, art, etc.

24)   BE GOOD TO YOURSELF

You deserve it. Make sure to do something you like on a regular basis. Treat yourself to a movie, an ice cream, or buy the new clothes you want. Go for that trip you have been putting off.

25)   WISH EVERYONE YOU MEET PEACE

In place of thinking angry or negative thoughts about people, wish them peace. Do the same with yourself. I don't necessarily mean verbally (out loud), but at least think it to yourself. Some people may not take it well if it is said out loud. Others might really appreciate it. Use discretion.

26)   EAT RIGHT

Stay away from sweets and other foods that contain *sugar* which is a *simple carbohydrate.* Simple carbohydrates worsen both depressions and highs. Rather, eat *complex carbohydrates* which are found in foods such as whole grain breads, brown rice, vegetables, nuts, seeds, and foods made from whole grains in general. The lower the carbohydrate count in foods you eat, the better. In many people, carbohydrates trigger the insulin response or overproduction of insulin in the body which causes tiredness and feeds depressive symptoms. Be sure to get adequate amounts of protein and vegetables. Also be sure to get an adequate amount of fiber and fluids. (See the Diet chapter for more details on eating healthy)

27)   PLAY, HAVE FUN

When is the last time you did something just for the fun of it? Those of us who are busy with several projects sometimes forget to have fun. *Scheduled type* people can schedule a time for fun and exercise. Often, if we don't take time for fun, we work ourselves sick. I have heard play described as *a suspension of the rules*. Think of children. Is this not how they play? They ignore the rules and just have fun!

My nephew, Tommy, and I decided to do some finger painting. I recall vividly when my nephew stuck his (whole) hand in a glass *full* of water to wet his *finger*. The water spilled out all over the table. Tommy looked at me and smiled and started laughing. I looked at him with a smile as I thought to myself, "What a way to react to making a mistake!" What a posture towards life. Then Tommy and I broke some more rules and decided the paper we were painting on wasn't enough fun so we painted each others faces. What a wonderful time. Can you imagine what we looked like? If you forget how to play, just hang around a child and let them lead the way.

28)   MUSIC AND ART

Listen to relaxing, healing, joyful music. Music is food for the spirit. If you can play an instrument, by all means, play it. More visually inclined people might prefer to draw a picture, go to an art gallery or just spend time appreciating God's artwork in all of nature and the beautiful world around us. The majestic clouds, a sunrise, a flower, birds, ducks, squirrels —they can all bring such joy. Depression has a hard time hanging around when joy arrives.

29)   SING

Play a song you love and sing with it. Music and singing help dispel fear and anxiety, and they fill your heart with joy as well.

30)   LAUGH

Laugh fear and anxiety away. We can make jokes about our fears, and watch them fade away and lose power over us. Laughter releases good feeling chemicals in our brains and bodies. A good belly laugh even massages our internal organs.

31)   ACCEPT

Let's accept ourselves as we are and others as they are, with good points and bad. No one is perfect. Acceptance is the fertile soil where love and happiness grow.

32)   THE PAST

Recall past accomplishments! Get strength and confidence from your successes of the past. Say to yourself, "If I did it back then, I *know* I can do it again." One word of caution: as you recall your past achievements, gain strength from them, but don't live in the past.

33)   HOPE

Find something to *hope* for. Schedule a get-together with a special friend. Organize a party for next month. Plan a vacation. Plan to go to a movie. Reflect every now and then on those fun plans to come. *Hope* is the opposite of depression. Depression is a feeling of hopelessness.

34)   VENT PROBLEMS

Vent problems by talking about them with friends and family members who understand. Even better, talk with a therapist. Therapists are equipped with techniques to help people heal. Join a support group where there are bound to be people with similar feelings. If there is no one around, write your problems down.

35) BREATHE

Learn to breathe correctly! Use *proper* breathing as a relaxation response to stress and anxiety-producing situations. Breathe in and exhale fully from your lower abdomen. You'll be amazed at how this will help you control your emotions and calm you down. It is a good idea (unless you are doing aerobic exercise) to keep your mouth closed and just breathe through your nose. When you breathe through your nose, correct breathing happens more naturally. Breathing properly can help dispel stress and depression.

36) STRESS COURSE

Take a course in how to manage stress. Since bipolar depressives who are under excessive stress have a 453% higher rate of relapse, we would do well to learn what causes stress and how to deal with it. This book and many of these tools will help, but there is also much more information available on the subject of stress management.

37) FOLLOW YOUR DREAM

We must follow our dream —our calling. How can we be happy if we do only what others want us to do? How can we be happy if we follow our parents' dream for our lives, instead of our own. Let's follow our dream.

38) A STORY

There was a boy whose father wanted him to become an engineer. The boy loved to read about psychology and study people. His father had a bad experience with psychology and so he discouraged the youth in that area. After suffering through years of engineering school, the young man received his engineering degree. His father was proud of him, but the young man was not happy. He proceeded to work several years as an engineer. Although he made pretty good money, he was not happy.

After reading dozens of psychology/self-help books, he then went to school to get a masters degree in counseling. It was hard work, but he loved every minute of it. He found that more than anything, he liked to do public speaking, writing, and offering hope to those unloved, discouraged and depressed. He is now living his life instead of his father's, and he is quite happy.

39)   CONFESSION

Exaggerated feelings of **guilt** are often a major concern of those suffering from depression or bipolar depression. It can be immensely helpful to go to confession if that is part of your faith. Or, as the Bible tells us, *confess your sins to your brothers and sisters*. This could be a trusted friend, sharing with a therapist or sharing at a support group such as a 12 Step Group. The sharing must be done to a non shaming face in order to heal. We need people to accept and love us, not make us feel worse. Feelings of guilt can be relieved through confession. If we have truly wronged another, then we would do well to ask for forgiveness and make amends to that person if possible. Guilt, I've had you to the hilt. It's about time that you've been spilt.

40)   SELF-KNOWLEDGE

We must acquire self-knowledge and awareness to grow and heal. We must learn how our behavior is affecting ourselves, and our relationships with others. It is wise to acquire self-knowledge at a moderate rate. Too much awareness too fast can be devastating, or at least increase our stress and anxiety. It can even increase what we are trying to get rid of: depression. Moderation is the key.

41)   CREATIVITY

I believe that as human beings we must create. It is deeply enjoyable and exciting to make something, create something. Creativity counters depression.

42)   IMAGINATION

We can use our imagination to create whatever we like. We get so used to doing things *by the book* that we forget how powerful imagination is, both as a coping tool and for creative enjoyment. We can imagine how we will be when we are more healthy, and then work toward that goal. We can use our imagination to create a beautiful scene, take a trip over seas, or even to adventure into outer space. Most great inventions, works of art, books and music, nearly everything was imagined before it was created or achieved!

43)   CURIOSITY

Curiosity is one of the three characteristics of genius. The natural curiosity children are born with makes them quick and avid learners. We are all born with this powerful tool. Where did it go? Maybe we shouldn't slap the child for touching things that shouldn't be touched. Maybe we should let go of our *things* instead of suppressing the gift of curiosity.

We wonder why we are a depressed culture. Yet we suppress or *depress* so many of the characteristics that make us human and healthy, such as our curiosity.

44)   SPACE

Sometimes we need space when we are depressed. By *space* I mean—distance from life's pressing concerns and all of the usual demands that are put on us. If we allow depression to occur and give ourselves this space and nurturing instead of quick fixes, the depression duration will most likely be shorter. Unfortunately, the space I am talking about is hard to get outside of a hospital setting. If it is a good hospital though, with a whole-person approach to recovery, it could be the best place to be when experiencing a severe depression or bipolar episode. Many good insights and changes can come in this time of growth—if we allow it to happen instead of trying to run from it or only medicating ourselves. Why not learn the lesson our depression (pain) is trying to teach us. As we learn these lessons, the depressions will become less frequent and intense, and our lives will become more peaceful and enjoyable.

45)   WRITE

Writing is a great outlet for me. It helps me to *clarify* whatever situation I am in. Writing is also a way to express creativity, a way for me to be me—since no one can stop me from writing whatever I wish. It is a form of meditation for me, and a way to pray. Writing helps get difficult feelings out. They go from my heart to the paper and in the process I am transformed.

46)   SUNLIGHT AND FRESH AIR

Be sure to get enough sunlight and fresh air. It has been found that sunlight affects our moods. Swiss health codes require 4 hours of sunlight daily in every room of a house when it is built. An Italian proverbs says: "Where the sun doesn't go, the doctor goes." A sunny house is a healthy house. Of course, too much direct sun can cause problems too. Moderation is the key. Serotonin, the feeling-good brain chemical, is present on the retina of our eyes and is stimulated by sunlight. It has been found that 2 hours exposure to bright early morning sun daily can be very effective in lifting depression.

Studies show that bright full spectrum light helps those who suffer from depression and bipolar depression (when in the depressed phase). Full spectrum fluorescent bulbs that help depression can be found at most lighting supply stores. You may want to buy several, for your home, office, or both. They are not too expensive and can bring a large payoff in the way you feel.

So many of us live and work in offices. To me, this is like living in caves. The lighting is not sufficient or natural. Most of us have experienced leaving an office building to go out for lunch and having to squint upon reaching the *natural lighting* of the outdoors. Another example is coming in from the bright outdoors and not being able to see well for a while because of the poor office lighting. Could this lack of natural light be affecting our health and our moods?

People working in offices would do well to use their breaks and lunch times to get out into the bright sunlight and fresh air. Why not go for a walk, too?

47)   FEEL

We must allow ourselves to feel what we feel, instead of denying or repressing our feelings. Don't repress it, express it! Express it in healthy ways though.

All feelings: *love, anger, hate, joy, sexual desire, curiosity, wonder, sadness, fear, loneliness, jealousy* and *pain*, usually carry with them a lot of energy—e-motion or energy in motion. If we realize this and redirect potentially harmful energy, we can do immense good with energy from *seemingly* negative sources such as *anger, fear, jealousy, pain,* and others.

48)   ANGER

Anger *mismanagement* often plays a strong role in depression and bipolar depression. As mentioned earlier, depression has been termed *anger turned inward* and mania *anger turned outward.* How then should we deal with our anger? How can we manage our anger and avoid expressing it as depression or manic behavior? Can we even make anger our ally?

As mentioned earlier, anger is not wrong or a sin. Anger is a feeling we have. Feelings are not right or wrong, good or bad. What is important is what we do with them. Feelings tell us things if we learn to listen to them, feelings have much to tell us. Anger is a God-given emotion that tells us we have been, or *are being* violated in some way. Anger is meant to help us protect ourselves. Immense energy often comes with anger. If we deny our anger or try and suppress it, it can do us harm in the form of illness (backaches, headaches, other physical sickness or mental illness). We may sabotage our relationships as we *act it out* in covert ways (the cold wars). Or if we carelessly and outwardly express our anger, we might do others harm. What then, do we do with our anger?

94

What do we do with our anger?

A.   First, allow ourselves to experience our feelings and accept that anger and all of our feelings are OK.

B.   Then we can ask, "What is this anger trying to tell me?"

C.   Then we can meter-out our anger and accomplish what it is telling us to do.

Funnel the fury

D.   Always keep *love*, the best interest for *all*, as the guiding force for the anger-energy.

E.   A person can add fuel to one of two fires:

   1. The fire of one's angry thoughts
      Such is accomplished when one dwells on one's angry thoughts. Doing this only hurts one's self, and any relationship one is engaged in. This fire often burns out of control.

   2. The "warm" fire of peaceful, loving, and forgiving thoughts.
      This fire burns evenly and generates heat to keep
      comfortably warm.

   The choice is ours.

The following page is a simple illustration of how we often do angry things without even realizing we are angry.

95

Person 2: "You look angry."
Person 1: "I'm not angry!"
Person 2: "Then why are you hitting me?"

1   **2**

Person number 1 has a problem with *lack of awareness* and *acting out*. When we repress our anger and don't express it in healthy ways, we often express our anger by *acting out*. When we act out our anger, we are not even fully conscious that we are angry.

Please note that the hitting is most often done *psychologically*, using words, body language, tone of voice and hurtful behavior as the *hammer*.

TEACHINGS ON ANGER

Gandhi spoke of using the power of anger for good. If one could learn to harness and transform the energy of anger, one would have a force great enough to move the world. Gandhi did just that!

He transformed his anger through prayer and self-discipline into a powerful force that he used to fight the British Government. Yet, even while fighting them with every *nonviolent* means at his disposal, he loved and respected them through the whole process. Some would call this *tough love.*

"Hate only hurts the hater"

Peace Pilgrim
*Peace Pilgrim Her Life and
Work in Her Own Words*

If someone does something to make us angry:

> We must address their behavior,
> but we must not hate them.
> We must pray for them, love them.
> We must be kind, but firm with them.

Author

"You should never try to talk to someone who is angry, because that person is not rational at that time."

Peace Pilgrim

I only agree with the preceding quote if the anger is truly out of hand and has taken over the person's mind. If a person is angry, but still rational, I attempt to communicate with them. I have learned much about other people and about myself this way. People often hold things in that they need to express. Often these important things are only let out when they are angry. Let's try not to fuel the anger, though. Use the anger-energy to resolve the problem. Do not try to conquer, control or manipulate the person.

**Use anger-energy to resolve
the problem
NOT to conquer the person.**

"In your anger, do not sin"

Ephesians 4:26

"Don't let the sun go down while you are still angry."

Ephesians 4:26

Remember that Jesus turned over the tables in the temple when He was angry. Jesus also responded to the Pharisees who were always badgering Him with the law (meanwhile neglecting love) by calling them "hypocrites and whitewashed tombs." When you read other passages in the Bible, however, it is clear that Jesus was patient. He channeled His anger using the utmost love. When He corrected people so strongly it was because they were clearly headed for destruction with their attitudes and ways of life.

Matthew 23:27 - Jesus

"Pray for those who persecute you."

Matthew 5:44 - Jesus

"Let no man drag you so low as to hate."

Martin Luther King, Jr.

**Our anger is there to
protect us
from those who don't
respect us**

98

Anger untamed
is a lit match
in the hands of a child
sitting in a pile of straw

Dwelling on Anger
is like piling
wood on a fire place
until the house burns down

"Forgive us our trespasses as we forgive those who trespass against us." This is not just part of the "Lord's Prayer." Personal experience has taught me that this is the way it is! *When I have not forgiven, I have experienced anguish and no peace.* The more I forgive, from the slightest to the harshest offenses, the more I am forgiven and the more I experience inner peace.

Another very important thing to learn about anger is that it usually happens when someone has crossed our *boundaries*. If a person gets angry regularly, it often indicates that they have boundary problems. A boundary is like a fence. It protects us from people who might hurt us or take what is ours. *People who have good boundaries rarely get angry* since their emotional selves (as well as their physical selves and possessions) are protected from trespassers. *Boundaries are needed to protect more than merely physical things!* There will be more concerning boundaries later.

A final thought on anger. There is usually an event or person who *triggers* our anger. It is important to identify who or what those triggers are. Then if the anger is very strong, we can get away from the trigger. We can get away, get perspective and get healed, before exposing ourselves to more hurt. We can then re-enter dialog with that person when feelings are less charged. I highly recommend reading *Make Anger Your Ally*—an excellent book on how to manage one's anger effectively (See Appendix B).

49)   INNER CHILD WORK

Inner child work is a method of getting in touch with feelings and memories we had as children that we might have repressed or suppressed. Those feelings or memories might still be affecting our behavior on a subconscious level today. A person can get in touch with painful memories that have not yet been grieved and actually do the grieving in the present. This helps set one free from acting out these *locked up feelings* in the form of inappropriate behaviors as adults. John Bradshaw, as well as many other therapists, offer inner child workshops.

51)   SELF-ESTEEM

Anything done to increase one's self-esteem will also moderate the cycles of a person's mood swings. A course on improving self-esteem or a good book on the subject can be helpful. But, one must not just read; one must take action to improve, and *apply* the principles learned. See Appendix B for an excellent book called *Self Esteem*.

52)   ELIMINATE

Sit down and make a list of all tasks being done and all activities going on in your life. Put stars next to the most stressful ones. Eliminate these if possible, or resolve to change them (or your attitude toward them). Next, eliminate *all* but the necessities, the things that must get done. Then number and prioritize those. Use the free time created to rest, play, meditate, or to engage in other life giving, spirit-feeding *tools* which are mentioned in this chapter.

53)   TRUST

Practice trust whenever possible. Pick the people you intend to trust carefully, though. Pick safe people, people who will respect your confidence and not gossip about you behind your back. Practice trusting people—at least with little things. If they prove trustworthy, try bigger things. Above all, trust God.

54)   FRIENDS

Get some good friends. Be sure to have more than one good friend. No one person can meet all of our needs. Friends have been a very powerful force in my recovery. Friends accepted and appreciated me in ways my family did not. My friends never labeled me or saw me as sick. Certain friends gave me *consistent* caring. Tears fill my eyes as I write this. Tears of appreciation and deep gratitude. Thank you Wayne, Tom, Juan, Jim and Joanna, Joanmarie, Miriam and Dawn. Your powerful consistency and caring helped lessen my huge mood swings with the anchor of your great love.

Remember, if you want a friend—be a friend.

55)   EXPECTATIONS

Lower your expectations of others and yourself a little. Know whom to trust and who can be counted on. *Expect* from these people, not from people who have let you down many times before. Do you know what crazy is? *Crazy is when you get treated poorly by someone 9 times and then you go to them the tenth time and expect to be treated differently.* Learn who to trust and who not to trust. Learn who to go to for help and kindness and who to avoid.

56)   EMPOWER YOURSELF

Take steps to help yourself heal. *Don't sit and wait for solutions*! Use your determination to find them, or create them.

57)   FAILURE

Does such a thing exist, or is what we call *failure*, just a learning, growing experience? Watch a child make a mistake or *fail*. What does he do? He laughs! I learned this from my 4-year-old nephew, Tommy. Thanks Tommy, you have taught me so much.

58)   BOUNDARIES

In a previous section, I promised to say more about boundaries. Boundaries help us to protect ourselves and our treasures. Imagine that we had no doors on our houses and no doors on our refrigerators. Animals would come in, ravage our houses and eat our food. They would use our couches and beds for nests. They would defecate in every room! Would you want to live there? Might you be a bit angry with that?

You may have had similar things happen with humans and know exactly what I am talking about. Boundaries are like fences that guard our treasures. Our treasures are our bodies, our emotions, our hearts, our minds, our values, our preferences, things that uniquely make us happy or sad, our beliefs, our spirituality, our souls, *our selves!*

Each of us has the right to say NO when someone transgresses or tries to transgress our boundaries by touching, taking or trampling one of our treasures. Here is an example: Sally highly values promptness. Hence, promptness is one of Sally's treasures. Peter knows Sally values timeliness, yet he constantly arrives late. Peter always *seems* to have a good excuse. Peter is trampling on Sally's treasure. Is Sally wrong if she gets angry? Of course not. However, if Sally continues to put up with Peter's irresponsible behavior, she will become angry on a regular basis and will look like the one with the problem. In a sense, she does have a problem. Can you see what it is?

Jane knows Peter, also. Jane is similar to Sally and values promptness. Peter arrives late for his first date with Jane. Jane feels a little angry and informs Peter that she values and needs timeliness. Peter arrives late a second time. Jane refuses to go out with Peter since he was not respecting her need for timeliness. *Jane's anger quickly dissipates as she engages in an act of self-respect* (Jane sets a clear boundary). Does Peter return? Some Peters do return, and they return on time! Other Peters find someone else to trample on. In either case, Jane does not continually date a person who does something that gets her angry. Thus, *Jane has self-respect and is whole.* She does not split her anger off by denying that part of herself. Nor does she feel alone as we often do when we sell our values just to be with someone, even if they don't treat us right.

Of course, no one is perfect. We would do well to prioritize and enforce that which is most important to us. We must *communicate* our values and treasures in our relationships. Others can't read our minds!

We must value ourselves and our treasures. We must be willing to let go of what is not good for us if we ever want to find what is good for us. The above example can be transferred to many other issues involving boundaries. A full explanation of boundaries would fill a book. People who suffer from depression and bipolar depression often have boundary problems! I highly recommend reading a book on boundaries. Developing healthy boundaries is a major step in recovery. Keep in mind that, as well as we want people to respect our boundaries and our NO—we ought also to respect other's boundaries and their NO as well. (See Appendix B for a good book titled, *Boundaries*.)

59)   FREE WILL

We have a free will, and we must exercise it. When other people or events are always controlling us we can get sick. This is especially true if we permit others to control us in ways that are contrary to our beliefs, and to what is right and true.

60)   WALK

To increase your energy when feeling lethargic, take a walk. Unfortunately, most people eat a candy bar when they feel like this. It has been found that walking brings about higher energy and lower tension than snacking. There is another problem with eating candy. Since it is filled with refined sugar, candy first raises blood sugar and increases energy. Then blood sugar plunges and with it—your energy level. On the other hand, walking *burns* calories, rather than putting them on. Walking is also enjoyable. If you have a low blood sugar problem to begin with though, you may need to have a snack of protein, vegetables, nuts or seeds before you walk.

61)   CHANGE

Change is actually what these TOOLS are all about, change and growth. In order to heal, we must be willing to change. Sometimes this will involve small changes such as getting to bed on time and getting enough sleep. Other times it will be necessary to make major life changes in order to cope, especially without drugs. Such a change might be leaving (or distancing from) primary relationships in which people have abused us. I have made many changes in my life to get to my present stage of healing. Are the changes worth it? You bet they are! The gains *far* outweigh any losses.

62)   CRY

It feels so good to cry. Crying relieves much pent up tension. My father used to tell me, "Never be afraid to cry, women live longer because they cry." I have taken Dad's advice. We'll see about living longer, but it sure does make my life more peaceful now.

As a man, I have found that it is wise to make sure one cries around people who understand. Our society has not matured to the point where a man can cry as freely as a woman and still be accepted as OK.

One other word about tears. It feels good and it is healing to cry tears of grief due to loss and letting go. This type of tears leads to acceptance and moving on. However, tears of woe-is-me and tears of self-pity often do not feel good, and they often never end. Although the latter type of tears may flow, the person usually doesn't feel any better.

63)   FAMILY

It is sad to say, but very often our families are the cause of our pain. Although, when a family functions well, it is a marvelously strong support system. It is my hope that families that are not healthy, for whatever reason, will spend some time learning what it takes to make a family work well. The family is the *foundation* of our society and civilization. If we heal ourselves and our families, the healing of the nation and the world *will* follow. If our *foundation* keeps disintegrating, I am scared of what is going to happen to the building that it holds up. We must get our priorities straight and stop putting everything else before our families. Things that are often put before our families are: our careers, our jobs, our independence, material things, money, Monday night football and especially our pride. We would do well to put our pride aside, and instead, love and support each other in our families. We ought to work things out, instead of just leaving when things get tough.

There is an exception. When a family is extremely dysfunctional and its members are continually hurting one another, one must distance oneself. Ideally one ought to distance oneself for a time and get help to heal *apart* from their family. Nevertheless, one should not lose total contact with one's family. Such a person should remain loosely connected with their family, while getting most of their needs for *healthy nurturing* met elsewhere. Research has found that those who maintain some connection with their dysfunctional family do better than those who totally leave their family.

Let's *learn* what it takes to make a family work well.
Let's not just *assume* that we know!

64)   DISTRACTION

Sometimes it is good to experience a little distraction, to get one's mind off things. See a good movie. Play a sport. Go to an amusement park. See a play or concert.

65)   LIVE WITH OTHERS

Are you lonely? Does loneliness depress you? Why live alone? Why not share a house or an apartment? It eases one's financial burdens, makes life more interesting and provides the companionship we all need.

66)   LABELS

Don't accept a label. Don't let anyone label you. It is so easy to get stuck when we allow ourselves to be labeled. People often live out the behaviors of their label instead of growing and healing. A person is much more than a label. I am not a codependent. **I am a person** who is healing from codependent behaviors. Instead of saying, "I am a *manic depressive*," it might be more healthy to say, "**I am a person** who suffers from *manic-depressive* type of thinking and behavior."

Do you see the difference? Behavior and thinking can be changed. Even in the very healing atmosphere of the support groups I have attended, some people label themselves. Often people want me to admit that I am *a codependent*. They say I won't heal if I don't admit it. I say bull. If I accepted labels I would be a manic depressive, an adult child of an alcoholic, a codependent, a paranoid and probably other things. So what am I? I am a person. Yes, of course I admit I have had, and still have some behavior that needed and needs to be changed. The process of healing deeply ingrained, unhealthy thinking patterns and behaviors may take a long time. However, it is possible.

There is a positive aspect to labeling. Labeling helps doctors, therapists and individuals to identify certain specific behaviors, symptoms and thinking problems. Once identified, one has a better idea as to which healing strategies to apply. Labels also help us to find books and support groups for a certain problem. We should label *types of behaviors and thinking* **not people**.

67)   DRINK

Drink lots of water and juices. Eat soups and vegetables. The idea is to get plenty of fluids into the body. Depression has to do with chemical and fluid balance in the body. *People who get depressed are often dehydrated.*

68)   TOUCH

Touching can be a major antidepressant. Most of us know how good a loving touch feels, but it seems that too few people give or receive this free antidepressant to one another. Touch can be a powerful healer.

There was a frightening and sobering event that happened during the Second World War concerning touch. A hospital didn't have enough nurses to care for all of its babies properly. It was found that babies who received no touch first became retarded and then eventually died! On the other hand, babies who received the loving touch they needed, thrived. If babies were affected so powerfully by touch, how might touch or lack of touch be affecting us as adults?

Touch can also be a way people use to control us (or we them) or to indicate another person's power. Your boss grabs you and asks you to do something for him. You would never grab your boss and ask him to do something for you. Do you see? Being touched in a manipulative way can evoke anger. Let us use the gift of touch responsibly and with love instead of just to control someone.

Treat yourself or someone else to a good massage. This kind of touch is invigorating for the mind as well as for the body.

69)   HUGS

It has been said that we need something like 14 hugs a day to keep healthy and happy. How many of us get half that? Let's start taking care of one another. It is respectful and healthy to ask for a hug rather than just taking it. Find out the people you know who like hugs and then indulge in this healthy activity. Remember, hugs don't have to be sexual. There is a cute and informative book called *The Hug Therapy Book* by Compcar Publishers. It is very short, concise, funny, and demonstrates the power of hugs as well as many different variations. Have a *hug party*. You'll fill the place.

70)   BACK AWAY

If a relationship is causing much pain, **back away**, get out of the spinning. Did you ever feel dizzy or confused in a relationship? When a relationship becomes unhealthy it is as if you are spinning around on a fast ride. If you get off the ride, the spinning will usually stop shortly thereafter. Moving off the ride might mean just backing away from the relationship a bit. Then things can be seen more clearly. Sometimes a relationship-triggered depression can be avoided this way.

71)   TIME ALONE

It is healthy to be with people. It is also healthy and necessary to spend time alone. Seek to balance the two. The time in which we live is a time of incredible over-stimulation. This takes a toll on our bodies, minds, and spirits. Time alone helps us to regain both energy and perspective.

72)   SCHEDULE

When you are depressed, it can help to schedule your day. It helps you get motivated when there is something that needs to get done and a time planned to do it. A schedule is kind of a contract with ourselves.

73)   WHEN IN DEEP EMOTIONAL PAIN

At this time, we can go in and re-write some of the destructive programming that we received as children. It is as if the heart is slit open during this time.

As an event in the present triggers our emotional hurts of the past, we have a golden opportunity to do repair on those areas in our brain that have stored unresolved hurts. An analogy might be: We are street repair men and women. We just turned down a street filled with potholes. It is now time to repair these potholes. If we didn't have access to the damaged street, how would we repair it? One way of doing repair is the use of strong self-affirmations. Affirmations like, "I am filled with peace, love, and joy. I am a loving person. I am OK. I am valuable just because *I am.*" Whatever works for you, use it. Of course, when one is in deep pain and feeling angry or worthless it is hard to speak kindly to oneself. Yet it is at this time that these affirmations are extremely powerful. In addition to doing this for yourself, spend time with people who really love you and who affirm you. You need to be emotionally cradled and rocked at this time in order to heal.

Applying forgiveness to both the perpetrator of the present as well as the past can have wonderfully positive healing results.

When the heart is open and in pain
that is the time to reprogram those pain cells

This is also a time to get into therapy and work on the issues at hand. One should also go to a support group. In these places, pain and strong feelings can be safely expressed and grieved. New information can be gained, such as new and healthier ways of looking at things. New skills are learned for coping with problems. The therapist also presents a new model of relating, one of loving support while you are going through your difficulties.

74)   EMOTIONAL INTEGRATION

When in deep emotional pain, our emotions are incredibly strong. If we give in to them, and the impulsive desires that often come with them, we could do damage to ourselves and others. As we learned in the CAUSES chapter, we need to be around people who love and accept us with all of our emotions, yet also set healthy limits on our behaviors. This helps us to achieve emotional integration. When we have achieved emotional integration, we accept and love ourselves with all of our emotions (even the scary ones like anger, hate, sadness, jealousy and fear).

To accomplish emotional integration, *our emotions need to be contained with love and limits.* For example: When you are angry, I do not withdraw my love from you, but I also will not let you throw a glass across the room. I am containing you with love and limits. We should have achieved emotional integration as children. However, if we have not, we can still achieve it as adults. As mentioned above, we can accomplish it in therapy, in support groups, and with any other people who love *all* of us. When our emotions are contained with love and limits, we integrate strong emotions into our *self*. We learn to accept ourselves and our emotions as OK. This relieves an immense amount of additional stress that can come from rejecting ourselves when we experience strong emotions such as anger. When you are loved with all of your stuff, then you know you are really loved.

75)   NAP

Naps reduce stress. This is a proven fact which is shown in several research studies. Naps also have an antidepressant effect for those who are feeling *down*, as well as a calming effect for people who are too *up*.

It is sad that in our culture napping is discouraged and looked down upon as weird or even as a sign of sloth. Rather, the opposite is true. Thomas Edison, for example, napped often in the midst of the developing of his innumerable creative contributions to society.

Napping is one of the most powerful methods which I use to keep emotional stability in this *swirling* society in which we live. Being a sensitive person in an often insensitive world filled with constant stimulation is not easy.

The most effective nap is taken whenever we feel a sense of overwhelming drowsiness. Although it is highly individual, naps usually last from 10 to 30 minutes. Napping much longer than this may interfere with nighttime sleep. Excuussse me (yawn), it's time for mine now!

76)   JOB HUNTING

It might be comforting to know that, "The American Disabilities Act of 1990, which applies to all businesses of 25 or more employees, bars employers from asking job applicants standard questions like whether they have a history of mental illness. Once hired, employees with these problems will be entitled to extra support and accommodation from their employers so long as they can perform essential job requirements. These rules were extended in 1994 to cover companies with 15 or more employees" (Milt Freudenheim, New York Times, 1990).

77)   THANKFULNESS

It is so important to be thankful, to spend time regularly in *thankfulness* for what we have, for our blessings. When sick, hurting, or depressed, it is so easy to let our pain become the focus of our life. It has been said that in most peoples' lives there are 90% good things happening and 10% bad. Unhappy people focus on the 10%. Happy people are those who focus on the 90% good. Some people keep a book called "I am thankful for..." Writing down things we are thankful for on a regular basis is very therapeutic. The list can then be reviewed when we have a hard time recalling what we are thankful for. Remember, *thankfulness and appreciation lead to JOY,* and *JOY is a major antidepressant!* It causes chemical changes in our brain. The ones that make us feel good. Let us count our blessings and be thankful.

78)   SYMBOLS

Use symbols to reinforce new habits or ways of thinking. When I made a decision to LOVE and not hate my ex-girlfriend (who did very hurtful things to me), I turned the peace dove on my neck around to face outward. This symbol has helped me to maintain that decision, and thus experience peace.

A friend of mine in Germany rearranged his whole room to help him get over a breakup with his old girlfriend, since they used to spend much time there. It helped him to let her go, and see things as new, not as they were.

79)   STRUCTURE

Bad thoughts sometimes seem to invade our thinking. It has been found that by adding *structure* to our life, bad thoughts are crowded out. Structure may be added by *scheduling* daily activities. These activities may include work projects that need to get done, as well as other things that we simply enjoy doing.

80)   SUPPORT PEOPLE

Just as *support groups* facilitate recovery, having *support people* also aids in the healing process. Support people can be healthy family members, extended family, or friends that know of our struggles. They understand what helps us and what does not. We should educate our support persons as to what we need in times of crisis. Then we should reach out when crisis occurs. Or even better, reach out as a crisis seems to be developing. We should have 3–5 people who are support people for us. This will insure that someone will be available when we are in need, and that no one person will get burnt out trying to help us.

81)   COMMUNITY

In our modern day age, we have a crisis of loneliness. One group's answer to that dilemma is *barn raising*. They adapted the idea from the Amish. For example, when a member wants to paint their house, other members who are available all come over and help paint the house. Thus, a big job turns into a fun community project. The members take turns meeting one another's needs, so all needs get met. Doing things together is almost always more fun than doing things alone. Human connection fights depression. Work together, play together, pray together. There are many other ways to experience community. Some people get involved in church groups, some help with extra-curricular school activities and others join political activist groups. There are numerous possibilities.

82) CHART FEELINGS AND THOUGHTS

I have found that using charts to list strong feelings as they occur, together with noting the thoughts that preceded those feelings, is very valuable. The very action of writing down the feeling and thought disrupts a negative thought process. Also, one can clearly see how negative thoughts lead to lousy feelings. Thus, one can replace them with positive thoughts which lead to good feelings.

On other charts, a person's highs and lows can be noted on a weekly and/or monthly basis. If there is a particularly tough time of day, month or year, charting will disclose the pattern. Hence, it can be anticipated and often avoided. See Appendix E for charts that may be copied, carried, and filled in as feelings happen.

83) LEEWAY

In our society today *efficiency* and productivity have become too important. We often leave no space for error or the natural surprise happenings that life brings us. We often leave no extra time between appointments. We use up all of our money and all of our emotional reserves, too. Thus, when surprises occur like an illness, death, traffic or car breakdown, we can't handle it since we have left no space, time, money or emotional reserves to cope with it. Leave space. Arrive early. Take one night a week just to relax. Don't spend all the money, save some.

84) COMMUNICATION SKILLS

People who suffer from depression and bipolar depression often come from families that have poor or even destructive ways of communicating. Hence, it is a wise idea to read a book and attend a workshop on healthy communication skills. It is also helpful to learn what typical communication looks like in dysfunctional families vs. functional families. *Facing Codependence* by Pia Melody and *Codependent No More* by Melody Beattie are excellent books to understand destructive

110

communication patterns in families as well as more healthy ways of relating. *Observation* is another excellent way of discerning healthy vs. unhealthy communication.

> **Learn communication skills.**
> **Communication skills are to a relationship**
> **what oil is to an engine!**

85)   SOCIAL SKILLS

In addition to having poor communication skills, people who come from dysfunctional families usually have inadequate social skills. Inadequate social skills damage our ability to *connect* with others socially. Having deep and meaningful connection with others and with society at large thwarts depression. Often depression is about a lack of connection. On the other end, having deep, meaningful and healthy connection with our brothers and sisters of humanity greatly facilitates healing. To obtain social skills, it is helpful to read books about them. Another powerful and fun way to learn is to observe people who *have* effective social skills *in action*. Then incorporate what you see into your repertoire of skills.

> **Time spent learning social skills**
> **is reaped in the harvest**
> **of an abundant life, filled with**
> **many friends.**

86)   LIFE SKILLS

Another area that is often lacking in dysfunctional families is *life skills*. By life skills, I mean the basic know-how of how to live and how to take care of oneself. Some life skills are: grooming oneself, keeping a clean house, shopping for healthy food, cooking, looking for a job, holding a job, saving money, balancing a checking account, making decisions, and finally, organizational skills. Many people need to learn or refine skills in these areas and more.

87)   NEW INFORMATION

When one grows up in a dysfunctional family, what one grew up with *seems normal* (even though it is actually quite unhealthy). Hence, in order to get healed, one important step is to acquire *new information* and learn what is more healthy. Congratulations! Reading this book is doing just that. However, don't stop here. Continue. Continue to observe healthy people in action. Continue to gather more information from books, tapes, talk shows and videos that will help you become more joyful, happy and help you to take the *dys* off dysfunctional.

88)   HABITS

The idea is to (over time) make many of these *tools* into habits, so that we do them naturally without having to think about them. Remember, they won't work if they're just read. They must be put into action.

Tools for a person experiencing an attack of too much energy or the up-side of bipolar depression.

When a person is experiencing the up-side of bipolar depression (often termed *mania*) he is like an exposed nerve. He is often extremely sensitive. Use the following tools and your common sense as to what you would do to protect that nerve from over-stimulation. Engage in calming and soothing activities. Shelter and protect that nerve from further damage.

Please note: Many of these are the same as tools for depression because unipolar depression and bipolar depression have a similar root for their cause. There are some important differences though, so please be attentive to them.

> **When a person is experiencing the up-side of bipolar depression he or she is like an exposed nerve.**

1)   THERAPY

When one is feeling real down and hopeless, it is often hard to motivate oneself. When we have energy, hope, and more confidence, this is a good time to seek therapy and explore what caused us to get down. A sad thing is that when a person is UP, he or she often doesn't feel the need for therapy. I think it is good that we don't let a **temporary** euphoric feeling deceive us. If a person is too high, talk therapy may not work without something to first calm the person down. This could be one or more of the tools that follow, or medication. Use whatever you are open to that works. First, use the tools in this section and *calming* tools from the depression tools section. If these tools aren't sufficient, don't be afraid to take some medication as prescribed by a psychiatrist to help you calm down and see you through the crisis. See THERAPY in depression tools section to learn more about therapy and seeking a therapist. Choose someone who knows how to treat the whole person—the emotional, social, psychological, and spiritual aspects of the person with bipolar swings—as well as with medicine (if medicine is needed).

2)   MEDITATION

Meditation causes a calming effect on the mind and body. It gives the body and mind a chance to replenish its anti-stress reserves. Meditation is a very powerful way of dampening the mood swings of bipolar depression, especially in the manic or high energy phase (see MEDITATION under depression "Tools").

3)   BREATHE THROUGH YOUR NOSE

Practice keeping your mouth closed while you are breathing. This prevents hyperventilation. It is believed that hyperventilation feeds mania. Breathe from your stomach and not only your chest. Put your hand over your belly button and breathe. If you are breathing properly you will watch your hand go in and out with your stomach. Breathing this way has a calming effect.

4)   EMOTIONAL DISCIPLINE

Let's make our emotions work for us instead of against us. If we let our emotions control us, instead of the other way around, we are in for trouble. When a person is very high, this is difficult to do without medication. If you can think well enough though, use your passion to put these tools to work. Use your intelligence to learn more about bipolar disorder and mania—the term often used to describe the high-side. Use the power you feel to attain self-control. One who has self-control knows true power.

5)   FOCUS

Learn to focus the high energy on a creative project. See FOCUS under depression tools section. Focusing your energy can be very helpful. Focusing has a calming effect. It keeps one's thoughts from becoming too scattered (which feeds manic symptoms). If you focus your energy, you can get some very productive work done at this time.

6)   DIVERSITY

To focus too much energy onto any one "person" could be overwhelming to them. Learn how *not to* put too much energy onto one person. Rather, spread the energy over several people and/or creative *calming* type projects. Don't try to take on too many projects, however; that will increase anxiety and feed the high.

114

7)   EXERCISE

Get some good physical exercise. Get tired. This way sleep will come easier at night. Exercise also helps us release much stress that is built up during a day. It helps clean out the pipes as the blood circulates more quickly. Sports are particularly effective. Since one must concentrate on the game, it has a meditative effect. Active sports like tennis, running, and basketball have the added benefit of naturally causing healthy breathing, which is calming even after the game. Social needs also get met while playing sports.

8)   SLEEP

Speaking of sleep, acknowledge that the less we get, the worse we will feel. Sleep is a must! Use whatever it takes to get enough sleep: exercise, meditation, relaxation techniques, nature tapes, etc. Stay away from drugs if possible. *But if necessary use them*—under the supervision of a doctor. Many sleeping medicines are addictive. Hence, use them for a short time only and under the supervision of a competent psychiatrist or doctor. Sleep is a must since research shows that *anyone* who goes without sleep for long enough will hallucinate and then become psychotic!

Some very helpful ways to get enough sleep are using *blinders* to cover your eyes, and using *ear plugs*. Be open to using these sleep helps. When a person is in this super-sensitive (*high*) state, the slightest noise or light can awaken them from a much needed sleep. Blinders and ear plugs are devices that protect our sleep time.

9)   SLEEP TINKERING

See SLEEP TINKERING in depression section. I have found it very powerful in helping level off the highs as well as the lows.

10)   SUPPORT GROUP

Find a support group with people who understand this feeling of so much energy, (and often so much anger). Such people are usually *accepting* and willing to share ways they have learned to cope. See SUPPORT GROUP in depression section. Also see Appendix A to find one.

11)   NEGATIVE THINKING

CRITICAL THINKING must be stopped. When on the up-side of a bipolar attack, one sometimes feels like a god and is tempted to act like one by judging everything and everyone. This temptation must be curbed. Critical

115

thinking must stop. Judgmental thinking must be checked. Just say *stop* when it occurs. Or better yet, use your will to turn criticism into praise and encouragement or just a simple wish of peace. We must be critical of others sometimes, but acceptance, encouragement, and praise must be given the majority of the time. Try 10% critical and 90% acceptance, encouragement, and praise. This is true verbally and action-wise, but we also must *think* this way too. Wrong thoughts can be damaging just as wrong actions—especially to ourselves, but also to others since we are all connected on the spiritual level. The criticism, anger or hate that I speak of which must stop is toward self as well as toward others. Persisting in this type of unhealthy thinking alters brain chemistry and may precipitate or perpetuate manic thinking and manic behavior.

12)   FEEL YOUR FEELINGS

Be aware if you are feeling your feelings or repressing them. I have learned that I have repressed a lot of anger. Depression is anger turned inward. Mania is finally letting it go—anger turned outward. Neither feels good. When depressed, I attacked myself. When high, I attacked others— verbally. The first caused me to lose myself, the latter to lose or at least hurt friends and family. I have had to learn how to notice when I am getting angry. When I notice, I allow myself to feel the anger. Then I ask myself what am I angry about? I then choose an appropriate course of action to deal with the anger. I talk to the person who I feel offended me, pray for them, write about it or do some very strenuous physical exercise if the anger is very strong. It's better to punch a bag or jog than to punch a person.

It seems that our society as a rule does not permit the expression of anger. Hence, anger expression is a common problem for many people. Other emotions are often repressed, too. We must learn how to feel our feelings and express them in constructive ways—and around safe people.

13)   REST

Rest, relax, re-create. When we are involved in recreation, the mind has a chance to re-create and rebuild itself. When we rest, it allows for the same. These three R's are as important as *doing*. Rest, relax, and recreate.

14)   WATER

Drink lots of water. It helps put out the fire. It helps our bodies and brains get rid of toxins and helps the delicate balance of the fluids in our body to remain in balance. Drink filtered water. The chlorine and other chemicals in our water have been found to be detrimental to our health.

15)   NAP OR SNAP

Napping is vital to someone who is in the throes of this state of seemingly endless energy. Common sense tells us that the body and mind must rest or it will break down. In the high phase of bipolar, night time sleep is usually greatly shortened. Sometimes people go without any sleep at all. Hence, it is imperative to capitalize on any opportunity to sleep, even if it is brief. The mood change is often dramatic. Napping will surely help a person who is sleep-deprived to be more calm and level headed. Families of bipolar sufferers would do well to *encourage sleep whenever it happens, instead of insisting that the sufferer sleep only at night.*

16)   HOT BATH

Recall the concept of *over-stimulation.* When a person is experiencing a *high,* he or she is like an exposed nerve. Picture how that exposed nerve could easily be over stimulated. It is as though the person is in constant stimulation. Taking a hot (or warm) bath is a great way to protect that nerve from over-stimulation. It is a great way to soothe that nerve. A bath is so relaxing. I think I'll go take one now.

17)   FRIENDS

Spend time around friends who are anchoring and calming for you. Spend time with friends who can accept you as you are. Avoid friends who you feel very agitated around. Avoid friends who encourage euphoric thinking. Avoid friends who drink or take drugs. Avoid friends who stay up all night.

18)   PEER COUNSELING

During this time when a person is in a high state, he or she is often very sensitive and very anxious. They often feel as though no one accepts them. Acceptance and being heard by a non-judgmental person at this time can be very healing. One excellent way of accomplishing this is through peer counseling. One way peer counseling may be accomplished is:
   A) Find a *safe* partner who is willing.
   B) Meet in a safe and private place (or talk on the phone).
   C) Set a certain time period say, 2, 5, 10, 15 minutes or more.
   D) One person talks and the other only listens. (The listener does not comment at all about anything that is said and tries not to be judgmental—even in his or her expressions.)

117

E) Reverse roles after the set time period. You may use a timer.

F) This may not be easy for some people, so you may want to begin with one or two minutes.

19)   DISTRACTION

When one is experiencing a high, thoughts are difficult to control. It can be most helpful to engage in activities that will help direct one's thoughts. Watching a good movie can help distract one from his or her otherwise obsessive or euphoric thoughts (providing that the person is not too distressed). An interesting but calm movie is suggested. Avoid wild heart- pumping thrillers.

20)   MUSIC

Calming music can be most helpful during anxious or high times.

21)   NATURE

Nature is so naturally calming. I have noticed that when I go for a Sierra Club hike my breathing actually changes. My body seems to take on the natural calm of the nature around me. Even when we cease hiking, I notice that my breathing is much more relaxed and natural. Hiking has many benefits: the natural tranquilizing effect of nature, social connection (when done with others), exercise, breathing, and the visual calming and joyful effect of the beautiful scenery. Some call it *nature therapy*.

22)   TRIGGER PEOPLE

It is imperative to stay away from people who are *trigger people* for us at this time. Trigger people are people we get upset around. Examples are: people who tease us, people who try and control us, judge us, put us down, and people who are negative and critical all the time. If you are not sleeping well at night, try and note who you were around. A person I know did not sleep well at night for 5 months. Shortly after he stopped seeing a woman he felt upset with often, his sleep returned to normal.

23)   MASSAGE (TOUCH)

Gentle touch or massage at this time can sometimes have a profoundly calming effect. Have a friend give you a massage. If you don't have a friend who will help you, treat yourself to a massage by a massage therapist. You are worth it! Another very relaxing touch is gentle tickling (running your finger tips gently) on a bare back, arms or legs. You can even do it for yourself—when it comes to your arms and legs. Of course it's more enjoyable when someone else gives you caring touch. You can also do a *trade* of gentle tickles with someone else. Be sure that they are a safe person and one who you know you can trust.

24)   MEDICATION

By now you know I believe in using alternative methods of healing whenever possible. However, if symptoms are really severe, *taking medication to get through a very difficult time is probably a wise course of action.* If one has symptoms such as: Not being able to sleep much (or not sleeping at all for several days), suicidal thoughts, large drop in weight over a short period of time, significant relational problems at work or home, spending huge amounts of money recklessly, or one is hearing voices or experiencing hallucinations, one is advised to see a psychiatrist and/or go to the hospital for immediate help and take the medication prescribed to stabilize oneself. Other symptoms one may have include: Pressured speech (inability to stop talking) and frequent angry outbursts.

Always receive therapy with medication. The idea is to look for the root cause of the episode. Consequently, the cause can be healed *or avoided* in the future. Some people believe drug therapy should only be temporary. They want to eventually reduce and get off their medication. Such people should be careful not to do so until therapeutic healing has occurred. Medication should not be discontinued until the crisis subsides and adequate support systems are put in place to maintain mood stability! Any change in medication should be accomplished with a psychiatrist's supervision. Medication is usually slowly tapered off rather than quickly stopped. This is done to avoid a possible withdrawal reaction.

There are very severe cases where certain individuals may need ongoing medication. Other people who are high functioning may be able to use therapy and other TOOLS to maintain mood stability without medication. Certain individuals can't or won't do the work that recovery takes to maintain stability without medication. For these individuals, it is better to take medication than go on disrupting their own lives, the lives of their families, and others around them.

25)   BOUNDARIES

At this time boundaries are extremely important. A person who is high is often ultra-sensitive. He or she may get angry quite easily. Thus it is wise to set boundaries to keep people from stepping on his or her sensitive areas. Much anger could be avoided if good boundaries are established by the sufferer as well as by their intimate friends and family. Refer to the *boundaries* section under *TOOLS for the depressed person* for more details concerning boundaries.

26)   RELAXATION TAPE

Relaxation tapes should be used at least once or twice a day during a high or manic episode. You can find relaxation tapes now-a-days in just about any bookstore or online at amazon.com or barnesandnoble.com. Relaxation videos are also an excellent idea.

NOTE: Most of the tools for depression will also work for a person experiencing the up-side of bipolar depression. Just leave out the ones that increase energy and concentrate on the ones that have a "calming" and "focusing" effect.

When I was immature, I used to enjoy euphoria. Now I offer my euphoric feelings up to God and He gives me peace. I offer Him my depression and He gives me joy.

Euphoria   → Peace

Depression → Joy

What a trade!

Chapter 5

HUMAN NEEDS

For Healthy Living

There are certain needs that human beings have which must be met in order to get healthy and remain healthy. Food, clothing, and shelter basics are far from adequate. That meets our physical needs. But what about the oh-so-vital other needs which are often neglected?

Areas of our being that need to be nurtured:

BODY
: Physical needs, food, water, diet, exercise, rest, sports. Simple physical activity.

MIND
: Study, read, intellectual challenge. Rest.

SPIRIT
: Play, creativity, prayer, music, art, charity, poetry, the need to love and be loved.

EMOTIONAL
: Hugs, be with people who love us and encourage us. To love and be loved.

SOCIAL
: Parties, get involved with a program to improve an area of social concern—environment, homelessness. Find something bigger than yourself which involves other people working toward the same cause. We must have a cause, a purpose to live for.

Mind

Body   Spirit   Social

Emotional

HARMONY

If I find myself not feeling too well, I take a look at these basic needs and at my life to see which I might not be getting. It really helps me to see quite quickly what I need. When I fill that need, I usually feel better.

1.   **BODY**

Air, Drink, and Food

Well, of course we need air to breathe. If we don't have air we won't last too long. In the past, this was hardly even mentioned. But with our environment being so polluted, it is becoming a more and more important health consideration.

As well as having healthy air to breathe, we need to *breathe healthy* to have good air. Quite often if a depressed persons breathing is monitored, it will be found to be shallow.

Tensing muscles is a way to suppress feelings. Try tightening your stomach muscles. Hold that, and try breathing. Where are you breathing from? Your chest? Isn't it hard to breathe like that? How long can you keep that up? Not long, huh? How did you feel when you were trying to breath with those tightened muscles?

So often we are doing just that, without being conscious of it. As a person begins to breathe more correctly, those repressed (somatized) feelings begin to surface. Practicing proper breathing is so important to both physical and mental health.

Proper breathing originates in the abdomen. First fill the abdomen with air and then if necessary, the chest. Exhale fully and slowly. Again, exhale the last breath from the abdomen. This may not feel natural and may

122

actually be difficult for a person who is so used to breathing only very shallow breaths from the chest.

Want to learn how to breathe correctly? Just watch how a baby breathes. Want to learn how to feel feelings and express them? Watch the beautiful expression in a baby who is angry or upset about something. The baby's whole body is involved in the expression of their feelings. How wonderful.

Where did this beautiful self-expression stop? Why did it stop? Who stopped it? It is important to watch a young baby before he or she gets shamed into repressing his or her beautiful emotions. E-motions are energy in motion. It takes work to stop these feelings from their natural expression. Tensing muscles is one way of doing this. Tensing muscles causes shallow breathing and shallow breathing causes muscles to tense, hence a vicious cycle is set up and perpetuated.

Breaking this cycle takes conscious effort until new and more healthy habits are learned. One might employ relaxation techniques such as yoga, progressive relaxation, visualization, and other techniques to begin to break the unhealthy cycle and replace it with a more healthy one. The origin of the repressing of feelings should be explored in counseling. One must find healthy ways of expressing feelings instead of somatizing them.

One may go for several weeks without food, but one will not live much longer than three days without water. Today, we must even question the safety of our drinking water. There are so many pollutants around that the water is chlorinated to kill viruses. Now it is known that the chlorine does us harm, too. It is therefore wise to filter chlorinated water. A filter is recommended that takes out not only chlorine but many other harmful pollutants. Spend a little time researching them. Invest in a good water filter and then experience the delicious taste of good water as well as the sure health benefits one receives from drinking plenty of water. Again, depression is often accompanied by or precipitated by a chemical imbalance in our systems which I believe is directly related to our bodies fluid balance. Quite often depressed people are dehydrated.

Next there is food. I believe that we are basically three things. We are what we eat and drink, what we think, and what we do. As for food, depression and other illnesses can be intimately related to our diets. People who get depressed are often people who have a problem with low blood sugar or hypoglycemia. Often they don't even know of the connection till years after depression has plagued their life, if they ever learn of it. As I have traveled further on in the recovery process, I note changes in my diet corresponding to my emotional well being. The more healthy I eat and drink, the better I feel. We'll get more into the details of diet considerations in the DIET chapter which is to come.

Exercise

The body is made of muscles which were meant to be used. When we use our muscles we feel good, that is, if we don't overdo it. When we are exercising or playing sports that are aerobic, we get the blood flowing faster and of course the heart is pumping harder to make that happen. So we are exercising our muscles, our heart, our lungs, and cleaning out our arteries a bit as the blood whizzes through them. I think of it kind of like a plumber flushing out the pipes to get better water flow.

As we exercise our bodies, we are giving our minds rest too; rest from the normal things it is involved in. We give time to recreate or re-create. We also can express or let out some of our aggressive emotions in a healthy way. A good hard game of sports can help release anger and pent up frustrations.

A study was done comparing Canadians with their Swedish counterparts who were in better shape physically. The study concluded that the Swedish were in better condition because they exercised doing things they liked to do. The Canadians (like Americans) exercised to keep in shape—not because they liked it. The result was that the Swedish exercised more, because they liked what they were doing (playing sports, hiking, etc.), and their psychological state of mind was better, too. Exercising was not suffering, but rather, a joy. Let's do what we like to do and ENJOY THE PROCESS. The goals will come.

Rest

Our bodies and minds are not meant to be buzzing along constantly. We need rest. Our system works more on rhythm than constancy. This can be seen as we observe our breathing. There is a kind of pause between inhaling and exhaling just as our hearts pause a bit between beats. We work, then we rest, work, rest. If we get in the right rhythm, we will make good music. If not, we will sound sour or even break down. Physical exercise seems to help our mind rest. When we are sitting and thinking (or just sitting), our bodies rest.

It is a good idea for a person who does physical work all day to read a book at night. A person who is using his brain all day, such as an engineer or writer (I could learn something here), would do well to play basketball or some other physically exerting sport after work. Keeping this balance actually helps us get more done. Meditation is powerful in that it is rest for the body and the mind. (see also SLEEP, SLEEP TINKERING, and MEDITATION in the chapter on TOOLS).

2.   MIND

Just as the body needs to be exercised, so does the mind. There is a saying that most have heard. "An idle mind is the workshop of the devil." Now it is certainly good to give our minds rest, just as our bodies. When the mind is rested, then it wants to work. If we do not give the mind a task to do, if we get bored, then temptations may arise to fill the void with thoughts that may be less than healthy. Most know this. Some of us are more inclined to physical work, but most know that it feels good to accomplish some mental work—passing a test in school, learning a new skill, writing a computer program. Others might enjoy learning a new language: Spanish, German, Russian. Still others would enjoy reading a good book. Whatever your choice, it is a good idea to give the mind the exercise it needs—as well as the rest.

3.   SPIRIT

Our spirits also need to be nurtured. By spirit, I don't only mean in the religious or faith sense. I mean the part of us that needs to laugh, the part of us that needs to play, the part of us that is not content with just surviving, the part of us that is not content with working all of the time and accumulating vast wealth. The spirit needs to sing, to dance, to make music, art, poetry. It needs to be creative, to look at the flowers and be filled with their beauty. It needs to gaze at the stars and experience wonder.

Look at a dewdrop on the edge of a blade of grass glistening like a diamond in the early morning sun. Diamonds are all around us and they don't cost anything, except a little of our time to notice them.

I believe that our spirit needs to pray. It needs to be one with the Creator in silence. It needs to be thankful to God for all He has given us— and even for what He hasn't given us. Our spirit needs to praise this Creator. It is in thanksgiving and praise, being thankful and praising God in ALL circumstances, good or bad, which leads us to acceptance, joy, and peace.

4. EMOTIONAL

We need to love and be loved. We need to feel we are worth something. We need to feel valued by someone, and we need to value others as well. Everyone needs to feel accepted. Most of us wish to feel part of a community. We need to be held and to hold. People need to be hugged and to hug, to be touched and to touch. We also need to feel our feelings and express our feelings, not stuff them in order to appear as a saint or a tough guy. Our individual feelings, and the way we express them, are one of the most telling signs that we are one of a kind. They tell of our uniqueness, yet they tell of our connectedness, our oneness. We all cry. We all laugh. We all feel pain and we all feel joy. However, different things cause these emotions to well up in each of us. Because of our uniqueness, we respond and express these feelings in our own special way.

5. SOCIAL

Often depression is about a lack of connection. Ideally we have connection with our families, extended families, and other groups and healthy individuals. Some families are quite dysfunctional and so we need to go out and form a wider family. Our churches, support groups, and other groups can serve this purpose well.

As human beings, we are by nature social. We need to feel that we are a part of something larger than ourselves, something larger than our immediate families. I believe that we have a need to contribute something to the human family. It may be volunteering for the fire department or doing volunteer work at church, joining a march for peace, or joining a group to save the environment. One might write a letter to the President or to another member of the government to let them know our feeling about a matter of concern.

Going to parties or pot luck dinners, etc. are healthy and "filling" ways to meet our social needs and the needs of others. Sometimes people get together to do unhealthy things which are either damaging to themselves or others. This type of social interaction certainly doesn't, in the long run, help the ones involved to be happier and healthier. In order to adequately meet our need for social life, the results must be life sustaining and life building for all involved.

Some counseling theories believe that we are damaged *socially* by our immediate families who are themselves hurting. Hence, healing occurs when we get into healthier social circles that treat us with respect, appreciation, and dignity. People from dysfunctional families have learned some very maladaptive ways of thinking and relating that are hurting them. Being in a healthy social atmosphere, we have the opportunity to watch, listen, and learn how to interact and think in healthier ways. Support groups serve a very powerful purpose here. They foster an environment that is usually safer than the outside world environment, while at the same time giving us a place to grow.

As human beings we need stable, committed, regular relationships. This provides grounding for us. We have something to look forward to. Some people have a set day that they meet every week. This is highly recommended with at least one person. It can be a time of sharing our stories; a time of mutual encouragement or some good fun.

Seeing that we get our basic needs (body, mind, spirit, social, and emotional) met and keeping them in balance is a vital part of recovery and healthy living.

Chapter 6

PREVENTIVE MAINTENANCE

Think Ahead

P icture the depression scenario like this. Depression is kind of like a *whirlpool*. When approaching the whirlpool, one begins to spin rather slowly around the edge. Continuing toward the center, things get out of control and one just spins helplessly around and gets sucked downward, unable to get out. Once so far in, it is virtually impossible to get out. At this point one must ride it out and let nature take its course, or take medication.

Imagine being in a ship traveling in the ocean, an ocean filled with whirlpools. We know, we've been this way before and have gotten sucked into a terrible deep whirlpool of depression. So what should we do? Wouldn't it be a healthy idea to navigate around these whirlpools? We must *tune in* and notice what is ahead! We must prepare ourselves for what is ahead.

One effective *preventive* idea is to begin every day with a time of relaxation. Numerous literature has been written concerning the immense benefits of relaxation. Relaxation exercises that slow the activity of our sympathetic nervous system have been found to be the most beneficial. This strengthens our immune system and calms the mind. It gives our body time to restore balance to its brain chemistry which was lost in daily activities, especially during stressful times of our lives. To achieve this type of deep relaxation one may practice meditation (see Meditation, under the TOOLS section in chapter 4).

Any of the techniques listed in the chapter called TOOLS can be used for preventive maintenance. As many as can be used comfortably

129

(without creating more stress) will help keep a person healthy. One must *balance*, of course, activities that feed the body, mind, spiritual, emotional, and the social needs. In my life, the tools which I use the most are:

1.   A time of daily, meditative prayer.

2.   A Support Group. I attend a support group called CODA (Codependents Anonymous) every week. This provides me with a place where I can say whatever I want without being cut off or judged. It allows me a safe place to express or let out my feelings without being shamed. I feel accepted for who I am by the people who attend. I also learn about myself and things (childhood abuses) that might have set me up for depression and codependence. I get to hear other peoples' stories of their hurt and feel compassion for them. New information is presented. I learn what healthy behavior is, and I learn what unhealthy behavior is. Once I know what each is like, I can distinguish between the two and choose to act in more healthy ways. It is an atmosphere of trust. I trust the people there and they trust me. This helps rebuild my trust which was so shaken. I get and give hugs, hugs of caring, hugs of acceptance, hugs of approval and hugs of love. I get and give looks of acceptance, looks of approval, and looks of love.

3.   Forgiving people who I feel have wronged me.

4.   Going to church on Sunday. This meets some of my spiritual and social needs, as well as giving me the chance to help meet the needs of others.

5.   Regularly allowing myself to feel my feelings. When I do, I express those feelings to people who I need to express them to. I also listen when others are expressing their feelings and encourage honest heartfelt communication.

6.   Working at regularly stopping obsessive thought patterns. When I start spiraling into thoughts of anger, I begin praying for those with whom I am angry. It isn't easy, but it works.

7.   If tempted with lustful thoughts, I just gently say, "I wish you peace" or "God bless you" (to myself) and then turn my eyes and thoughts in another direction. Now of course it is healthy to desire a woman and to be with her, in a healthy, holy, and timely way—such as in marriage. But persisting in lustful thoughts of one who is not our mate is not healthy and can alter brain chemistry in a negative way.

8.   Allowing myself to feel angry. If there is a valid reason for my anger, I will approach the person who I'm angry with and tell them how I feel, and why I feel that way. Others are free to express their anger with me, too.

9.   I almost never eat refined sugar or any food that contains it. I rarely drink or eat things that contain caffeine or alcohol since these chemicals contribute to mood swings. But I forgive myself if I slip. I eat lots of vegetables and fruits and drink lots of water.

10.   Scheduling in some fun. For if I don't, I probably wouldn't get it. I get fun and physical exercise playing volleyball once a week. Volleyball is also social. Consequently, I get social needs met as I play. In the summer I ride my bike often and go for walks, hikes, camping, boating, and more.

11.   Hanging around people who don't try to oppress me. I spend time with people I feel I can trust and who trust me.

12.   I have a *purpose* in life. Writing this book is a big part of that. Reaching out and helping others the way I have been helped and loving others as I have been loved is good maintenance work for me.

13.   Getting out in nature, sun, fresh air, and observing God's wonderful creatures takes me out of myself and fills me with joy and wonder.

14.   Rest. I get enough sleep and rest, too. If I don't get enough sleep at night, I make sure to take a short nap during the day when feeling tired.

15.   Living by my values and the teaching of Jesus to the best of my ability. When I don't live up to these values as much as I would like to, I have learned to forgive myself and be gentle, compassionate, and patient with myself. This helps me to be that way with others, too.

16.   Often reminding myself that *I am perfectly imperfect!*

17.   I choose my thoughts. When feeling depressed, I look at my thoughts and if they are bringing me pain, I change those thoughts to ones which bring me joy and peace. For example: Last night I was beginning to feel depressed. I realized that I was thinking of my girlfriend and how I could not be with her because she was so far away. I was feeling afraid of losing her. So I redirected my thoughts and began to sing a favorite Taize' song about non-fear and trust. Immediately my feeling of depression left me. I thought of the purpose I have in being where I am now, and the hope we both have of being together in the future.

18.   Once it occurred to me, that there have been times I have *set myself up* for a fall. This happened mostly in intimate love relationships, or rather in relationships where *love could have been possible* with time, patience, and nurturing. I, like so many other people, wanted to love and be loved.

Before I was married, when I met someone who liked me a lot, and I her, sometimes I lost it. I lost my sense of cool. I lost my patience and my sense of self-respect. I became consumed by my desire for the relationship. I often got into thinking way ahead, to the possibility of marriage. I thought of all the things we would do together. And probably worst of all, I bore my heart way too soon. So what happened? The person was blown away! They became scared.

When I was single, I met someone who liked me a great deal and I her. She saw all the good things in me and told me of them. She desired to be with me and kept approaching me, as if she could not get enough of me. In short, she put me on a pedestal. Wanting to be loved and admired, I let her do this. I fell for the bait—hook, line, and sinker. I let my heart go and opened it too widely to her. She became scared and broke up with me. This caused me incredible pain. However, some lasting lessons have been learned. *Don't let anyone put me on a pedestal.* Also, no matter how much it seems that someone loves me, *give those strong feelings the test of time* before opening my heart too much. *When I do open my heart, open it slowly* so I don't flood the one I love—as if a dam were breaking.

Setting oneself up can be done in many ways, such as putting *all one's hope* of getting work in a *single* job applied for. What happens if the job is given to someone else? Isn't it much better hoping to get it, but not depending on it and at the same time pursuing other options? There are countless other ways a person can set themselves up. Think of a way you do this. What can you do to avoid setting yourself up in the ways you do? Let's stay flexible and keep our options open. Let's make it a habit to have alternative plans, so if our desired plans don't work out we're not distraught.

19.   Live in the now! I find that I am so much more peaceful when I live in the now. Living in the present moment is the opposite of setting oneself up. It is instead, *building oneself up*, or building a relationship on the solid foundation of moment by moment sharing and being present to the person I am with. How can I be present to you when I am so busy dreaming about the future? It is good to dream also, but 10% dreaming and 90% presence is far better than the other way around.

20.   A favorite thing I like to do is to have pot luck dinners with friends. I like to eat and I like to be with friends. This is an inexpensive way to have a great social life while experiencing community and a good meal. Each person

132

brings their favorite dish. The variety and quality is often better than restaurant food.

The preceding are some of the things that I regularly do as a measure of preventive maintenance. They work for me. We all have our needs. If we meet them in wholesome ways, we will be able to lead quite healthy lives and deal with life's struggles as they occur, while avoiding painful and often unnecessary depressions.

It's not life's inevitable tragedies that stifle, overwhelm us, and cause us so much pain. It's the *"stuffing"* of them that does us in.

So let us allow ourselves to feel what we feel. Let's learn what our needs are, and get them met in healthy and loving ways. If ideas are needed, try going to the chapter on TOOLS. They will help. Of course we each have our individual needs. Each person must determine what these are for himself or herself. Accordingly, each of us alone is responsible to see that we meet our own needs. We set ourselves up for major disappointment when we depend too heavily on any *one* person to meet our needs. It is unhealthy to assume that someone else will or *should* meet our needs for us.

When our basic needs are met, then we can go out in charity and try and help others get their needs met.

Be Aware of:

Early warning signs of depression:

1. Feeling unhappy.
2. Beginning to lose hope, feeling like things will never get better.
3. Change in hygiene—no longer taking showers.
4. Social withdrawal.
5. Feel overwhelmed—too much to do, can't possibly get it all done.
6. Tiredness, fatigue.
7. Negative attitude toward self and others.
8. Feeling inappropriately afraid often.
9. Change in sleep patterns, sleep too much or not enough.
10. Early morning awakening —such as 3am.

If experiencing several or all of these, JUMP into action.

a) *Talk about your feelings.*
    - Tell a close understanding family member.

- Tell a close compassionate friend.
- If you have a therapist, tell him or her as soon as possible.

b) *Write your feelings down.*
- It can help so much to write down feelings and thoughts.
- On paper things often don't seem so bad.
- List all things that burden you.
    + Prioritize them 1–10.
    + Cross off all but things that must get done.
    + Directly address any particular problem causing you to feel down. Tackle it yourself if you can, or get help if you need it.

c) *Go to a support group.*
- That is what they are there for. ACOA, ALANON, CODA, AA, DMDA are some possibilities. See *Appendix A* to find one.

d) *Look at the basic HUMAN NEEDS in your life:*

Body   Mind   Spirit   Emotional   Social

Are they being met? Which ones are not being fed? Focus on them.

e) *Refer to chapter 4 which is filled with TOOLS to keep you out of depression.*

Be Aware of:

Early warning signs of the *high side* of bipolar depression:

1. Insomnia.
2. Racing thoughts.
3. High phone bill.
4. Change in hygiene—stopping to take showers.
5. Very talkative.
6. Poor appetite.
7. Taking on too many projects.
8. Argumentative.
9. Unrealistic ideas
10.Spending lots of money—usually carelessly.

If experiencing several or all of these, RELAX into action.

a) I say *relax into action*. This may sound easy to some, but to the High person this is probably one of the hardest things, but *most necessary* things to do.

b) *Tell a friend*, loved one, or therapist how you are feeling.

c) *Give it up*! Use discipline to let go of these feelings. Offer them up to God and ask for His peace. HE will help. To hold on to them and enjoy them only magnifies them.

d) *Focus* the energy on a creative project.

e) *Meditation* is so powerful in calming the highs. Sit with a candle and meditate!

f) Do your best to *eat and sleep right*. It helps replenish vital nutrients in the body.

g) *Don't take on too many activities*—let some go and focus on doing a few things well.

h) *Breathe through your nose*. Practice keeping your mouth closed while you are breathing. This prevents hyperventilation. It is believed that hyperventilation feeds mania. Breathing this way also has a calming effect.

i) *Let God be God*. Realize that you are not!

j) *Take a hot bath*. This is a wonderful and very effective way to relax.

k) *Stay away from sugar and caffeine*. These, as well as all other things ingested that tend to produce a stimulation effect, must be avoided!

l) *Let go of the high*. Make a decision to let go of the high feelings. It feels good, but remember, what goes up must come down, and it often comes crashing down! (See the TOOLS chapter for more ideas.)

Chapter 7

WHAT CAN I DO TO HELP SOMEONE WHO IS DEPRESSED OR HIGH?

B efore getting into what we can do to help, I want to highlight that people who suffer from depression and bipolar depression can sometimes be very manipulative. This manipulation can tear us apart if we let it, especially if the person is threatening suicide. Suicide threats are often extremely manipulative since the hearer will often do anything to try and prevent it. If a person threatens suicide, their threat must be taken seriously and a hospital or police notified. If it is a real threat, a hospital is the best place to be. If it is a manipulative move, they will learn quickly of the consequences for their tactics. Let professionals decide.

I have suffered immensely from being manipulated in such a fashion. Remember that you are not responsible for another persons' life! Each one of us alone is responsible for our own life. No one else is responsible. If I hear a threat, be it subtle or direct, I will let the person know that I care and hope they will not take their life. But the responsibility for that choice is theirs, not mine. I'll say, "I hope you choose life." Once, when I was given a suicide threat, I called the police. When they investigated the person threatening suicide, the person was sitting calmly watching TV while I was a wreck!

As I said, however, we must assume the threat is real and contact the police or hospital. Suicide hotlines can also be called (see Appendix A for a list). Some people do kill themselves. So don't take a chance. Now let us explore how we can help less severe cases.

There are several things which we can do to help someone who is depressed. I would like to offer some of the ones that helped me. When I was in a deep clinical depression, it seemed that nothing would help me. In retrospect, I can now see some things which did help. These things did not instantly take me out of my depression or high, but they did ease the pain a bit and they have contributed long lasting positive effects, even to this day. Some of the things I have found to be the most beneficial for myself, and for heading off a depression are:

1. ALLOW THEM TO BE DEPRESSED. It's not the depressed person's fault that he or she feels depressed. Don't tell the person to snap out of it.

2. SPEND TIME WITH THE PERSON. Just be with them in their suffering. This means so much. Just to let them know there is someone who cares enough to be with them through it is powerful. They may not acknowledge you immediately, but when they are better they will never forget that you stood by them. I know I will never forget those who suffered with me and prayed for me when I was down. If, on the other hand, the person wants to be alone, then let him or her be. Don't force yourself on the person. Encourage and offer, but don't force.

3. LEARN ABOUT DEPRESSION. Spend time learning about the disease. This book and others will help you to understand the person better, and learn what to do to help.

4. DON'T JUDGE! Depressed people are usually full of judgment. Often much of this harsh judgment is cast on themselves. Some people say that "Depression is anger [judgment] turned inward." It is so hard not to judge, because often we see so clearly their destructive thought patterns. We see the things that need to change to avoid future depression. Some of these things may be lovingly brought up in a non-judgmental way, as food for thought, but not harped on.

5. ACCEPT THEM AS THEY ARE. This goes hand-in-hand with not judging. Try to accept whatever they say. It may hurt at times. But this is *really loving*. It doesn't necessarily mean agreeing with them, just accept them. It is possible (but not easy) to accept and love others and yet disapprove of inappropriate thinking or behavior that is hurtful to us and/or themselves.

6. LISTEN. Often, just listening means so much. It gets things out that people need to get out. I say "just listen," but to really listen to someone is hard work. It takes discipline and effort that can only be accomplished by

love. If you cannot listen too well or if it is too painful for you to listen, try to get the person who is hurting to spend some time with someone else who is a good non-judgmental listener. A person who is in deep emotional pain is like a balloon that is too full of air. If some of that air is let out, the balloon has less chance to break.

7. ENCOURAGE THEM TO EXPRESS THEIR FEELINGS. At this time the depressed are usually paralyzed by their intense feelings. Encourage them to express their feelings to you, to a counselor or to some trusted friend. When they express their feelings be sure to validate their feelings as being OK. Remember feelings are not right or wrong. They are just feelings. Feelings need to be expressed. Unexpressed feelings can explode into depression or mania. If they cannot or will not share their feelings, encourage them to at least write them down in private.

8. LIGHTEN THEIR BURDENS. If there are things that can be done to ease daily burdens, do one or two. Take the garbage out. Baby-sit for her so she can go out and have some fun. Cook, do the wash, or wash the car.

9. BELIEVE IN THEM. Help them to see the value in themselves. Let them know how much they mean to you. Use subtle means to convey this. It will be easier for them to believe. People often don't believe compliments that are paid directly to their faces. Sometimes it is better to compliment a person behind their back, to someone you believe will pass it on to them.

10. KEEP YOURSELF HEALTHY. Remember, one person cannot do everything. Our love and care will not heal someone immediately. It takes time. So the person trying to help must take care of himself or herself, too. The logic is: If I get sick trying to help you, then I am no good to you anymore.

We would also do well to keep in mind that *we cannot love everybody.* Hence, we must focus our love on the special few whom we have enough time and energy to give our love to. If Joan tries to love *all* who demand her love, her love may be spread too thin. Thus, no one will be loved properly and her love will have little effect on anyone.

Guidelines for keeping yourself (the caregiver) healthy

DO:

⇒ *__Be sensitive to your own signs of being over-stressed.__*

⇒ *__Join a support group__* for families of Depression and Bipolar Depression sufferers. A lot can be learned from these groups. They also provide some powerful emotional support as well.

⇒ *__Tap into community support networks__*. Call your local mental health center, hospital, church or look in the local paper to find out what support is available. See Appendix A and F of this book for some excellent resources.

⇒ *__Give yourself a pat on the back__*. You don't have to stay. You don't have to be there for them—especially if they are mistreating you. Whatever you do is a gift to them (if it is done in love and not from guilt).

⇒ *__Treat yourself.__* Be good to yourself. You deserve it! Take that long awaited trip, or just get away for the weekend—a mini vacation. Do whatever you like to do. It's usually best to do light things, like going to a movie.

⇒ *__Seek help from friends__*. Seek help from several friends. Don't try to get all of the help from any one person. Be sure to express your appreciation for any help you receive.

⇒ *__Seek help from family__*. However, they may be too emotionally involved. If so, seek help elsewhere.

⇒ *__Seek help from church or synagogue.__* Ask for help at your place of worship. People are often glad to help. Ask for prayer, prayer is powerful!

⇒ *__Be sure to get your own needs met.__* You can't run on an empty tank. Don't just meet your basic needs. Be sure to find time to play and enjoy life. You will be a much better helper and a much less resentful one.

140

⇒ **_Read and learn all you can._** _Learn all you can about the problem. Self-help books and tapes, talk shows, magazines and seminars are good sources of information._

DO NOT:

⇒ **_Go it alone!_** _Get help for yourself. Depression and bipolar depression are very difficult things to deal with. Get Help. Preferably from someone who's been there._

⇒ **_Accept undue responsibility._** _Do not feel responsible for another person's feelings, thoughts, choices, behavior, actions or their situation. These things we cannot control in another person._

⇒ **_Get too close_**, _or you might get sucked into depression also._

⇒ **_Accept undue BLAME._** _When people are depressed or high they are usually in a lot of pain. They may unjustly blame those close to them for their pain, or for their problems._

⇒ **_Enable them_**. _They must feel the consequences of their actions or lack of action._

⇒ **_Feel guilty about taking time for yourself_** _You need time for yourself. The person hurting may want all of your time. Be sure you take some time for yourself. You'll be in better shape to help them if you do._

If there is a pattern of a person's dependency on us, there could be a problem of codependence. We might be feeding or enabling their behavior or illness. In this case, it would be immeasurably helpful to get involved with a codependency support group and to read a book on codependence. (See Appendix B for recommended reading list.)

11. HELP GENUINELY from the heart. Don't just help out of responsibility. It is much better to give a little _heartfelt_ help that is genuine, than a lot of help we don't really want to give. _Don't operate from guilt. Operate from love. Love is the only thing that truly heals._ Giving out of guilt or only to _be responsible_ merely pacifies ourselves.

12. DON'T PRESSURE THE DEPRESSED PERSON. Encourage him to seek help, but try not to add additional pressure to his already heavy load. We may not see the heavy load, he may not either. Rest assured, he is carrying a heavy one.

13. DON'T GIVE ADVICE unless the person asks for it. (And then give it sparingly.)

14. HUGS. Give the person lots of hugs. Hugs are healing. However, ask their permission before giving them a hug. Read *The Hug Therapy Book* listed in Appendix B.

15. PRAY FOR THEM. Prayer works, but we must be patient and persistent.

16. MIRROR their good qualities back to them. At this time it is unlikely the person can appreciate his or her good qualities.

John Powell, in his book *The Secret of Staying in Love* says:

> p55 "We are like mirrors to one another. No one can know what he looks like until he sees his reflection in some kind of mirror. It is an absolute human certainty that no one can know his own beauty or perceive a sense of his own worth until it has been reflected back to him in the mirror of another loving, caring human being."

> p58 "The basic cause of all mental and emotional illness is the inability to form deep human relationships of love."

> The word "all" in the above quote would be more accurate if it read "most."

To help someone see that they are valued and that they are loved are two of the greatest gifts we can offer to another person

---

17. SOURCES OF LIFE. Connect them with sources of life. Sources of life are things and people that build them up and foster good health and good thought.

18. THERAPY. Encourage counseling with a good therapist, and be supportive of their therapy. It could be immensely helpful to get into family therapy also, since there may be a family dynamic that is occurring which contributes to depressive or bipolar behavior.

19. HOPE. Rekindle their hope. Help them find a reason to hope.

20. LOVE THEM. Let them know that you love them now and always.

21. CREATIVE PROJECT. Get them involved in a creative project. Creative projects are sources of life and they heal the spirit.

22. NATURE. Bring them on a hike, or a walk in the park. Nature is healing.

23. PHYSICAL ACTIVITY. Do something physical with them. Play a sport, jog, etc. Do something that makes them sweat and keeps their mind actively involved as well.

24. BE AVAILABLE. Be available to them when they need you, assuming requests are made with respect and are within reason.

25. DON'T TRY TO CHEER THE PERSON UP. They may not be able to brighten up.

26. DON'T TELL THE PERSON HOW THEY SHOULD FEEL.

27. DON'T TAKE AWAY ALL RESPONSIBILITY.

28. DON'T BE AFRAID TO TELL THE PERSON YOUR PROBLEMS. Doing so will help them get their mind off their problems. It may also help them to feel *useful*.

29. DON'T ACT AS IF NOTHING IS WRONG.

WHAT CAN I DO TO HELP SOMEONE WHO IS ON THE UP-SIDE OF A BIPOLAR ATTACK?

Please note that helpful things for the up-side or "high" side are mostly the same as for the low-side, with some small differences. This is because bipolar is like a car that has weak shock absorbers. The car just bounces *up* and *down*.

The solution, in either case, is to install a good shock absorber. This helps smooth the sometimes rocky road of life. The malfunctioning shock absorber is poor self-esteem. Its replacement, the healing agent, is genuine LOVE. Love bolsters self-esteem. Love is what the following list is all about.

1. ALLOW THEM TO BE HIGH. Remember, it's not their fault! However, if they are in an extremely high state and destroying themselves or others, they may need to be forced to take medication. As a very last resort, they may need to be put in a hospital against their will to get them calmed down.

2. DON'T JUDGE! The person is often prone to be critical and judgmental. Often much of this harsh judgment is cast on themselves, as well as outward toward other people. It has been said that, "Depression is anger [judgment] turned inward." I see mania as "Anger [judgment] turned outward." It is so hard for *us* not to judge, because often we so clearly see their destructive thought patterns and behavior patterns. We see the things that need to change

to avoid future depression. Some of these things may be lovingly brought up in a non-judgmental way, as food for thought, but not harped on.

3. ACCEPT THEM AS THEY ARE. This goes hand-in-hand with not judging. Try to accept whatever they say, although it may hurt you at times. Acceptance is such an important part of true love. It doesn't mean you have to agree with them, just accept them.

4. LISTEN. Often, just listening means so much. It allows them to get things out that they may need to get out. I say "just listen," but to really listen to someone is hard work, especially when they are *high*. When the person is high, often they will talk excessively. So it is hard to listen. If we listen to them at this time, we may get a clue as to what is really bothering them. But we must be prepared for brutal honesty. This may hurt, as a lot of repressed anger often comes out at this time. That is why support groups are so valuable. One person alone cannot possibly listen all of the time to someone who is in a *high* state—especially if he or she is saying hurtful things much of the time.

5. VALIDATE THEIR FEELINGS. It can be so powerful to validate feelings for the person. Statements such as: "I see that you are angry about that. I would be angry if I was in your shoes too!" can help a person recognize his or her anger and know that it is OK. Another validating statement might be, "I see you are very hurt over what happened. Tell me about it." Often people suffering from depression and bipolar depression have not had their feelings validated as children. To validate feelings is to bring about healing. Encourage them to express their feelings. Then validate them.

6. BELIEVE IN THEM. Help them to see the value in themselves. Let them know how much they mean to you. Sometimes using subtle means to convey this will make it easier for them to believe. People often don't believe compliments that are paid directly to their faces.

7. KEEP YOURSELF HEALTHY. It is very easy to become consumed with the responsibility of taking care of someone that is ill. As a caregiver for a person who is in a manic or high state one can reach burnout very quickly. Knowing this, and guarding against *burnout* can make one a much more effective helper. Take good care of yourself! See **Guidelines for Keeping Yourself Healthy** in the previous section. Also, seek help. Do not go it alone.

Support groups exist for the *families* of depressed or bipolar sufferers. These can be a great comfort as well as an invaluable resource of information. If there is not one in your area you can start one. Churches and hospitals are usually willing to provide a room. Then just run an add in the newspaper to inform anyone interested of the time, place, and purpose of the meeting.

8. LOVE THEM. Let them know that you love them.

9. MEDITATION. Encourage it. Meditation gives the kind of calming effect that is needed to still the raging fire of an unsettled mind. Meditation helps to focus high energy levels toward accomplishing creative and worthwhile tasks. Be sure to engage in wholesome meditation. Some forms of meditation can be unhealthy. Use the basic rules for meditation found in the *tools* chapter.

10. HEALTHY PEOPLE. Encourage them to spend time with people who have healthy attitudes and healthy thinking. We truly do become like those we spend time with. Encourage yourself, as well as the person you are helping, to spend time with healthy people.

11. THERAPY (individual and/or family therapy). If the person is willing to go, therapy at this time could be very valuable. In addition, family therapy could shed light on family dynamics which may be helping to perpetuate the individual's behavior.

This section has purposely been shortened since there are so many things that are the same to help a person who is either depressed or high. Remember, we are dealing with bipolar depression, hence, both sides are depression. Therefore, the beginning of this chapter has many helpful suggestions that will work for the person who is in a high state, as well as for the person who is in a depressed state. Please refer to that section for ideas. Also, refer to the chapter on TOOLS that is filled with good ideas to help decrease mood swings on both ends of the spectrum. *Keep in mind that when a person is in a high state, the idea is to engage in activities that have a calming effect.*

Chapter 8

DIET

Linking Diet, Depression, Biochemistry,
Antidepressants, and Stress

I t has been said that we are what we eat. It is clear to me that what we ingest in the form of food and drink builds and sustains our biochemical bodies (including our biochemical brains).

Drink some alcohol. How do you feel? Is your thinking the same as before you drank it? Eat some ice cream. Eat some chocolate. How do you feel? Each of these and many other substances—caffeine, nicotine, etc.— cause chemical reactions in the body and many also cause chemical responses in the brain.

> **As surely as drugs we ingest alter our body chemistry, the food and drink we digest affects us.**

Few people choose the *dietary* road to health, either because they don't know about it, or they don't have the will and patience required to treat their depression through change of diet and use of vitamins. Actually, I believe that it takes more than just diet and vitamins to cure a case of major depression. However, diet plays an important role. In fact, research has found that refined sugar consumption contributes to depression.

Most *low blood sugar* symptoms are also exhibited in a person who is depressed or suffering from bipolar depression. Krimmel & Krimmel, authors of *The Low Blood Sugar Handbook* call one low blood sugar

147

symptom: *Dr. Jekyll and Mr. Hyde.* Krimmel & Krimmel also list *depression* as a symptom of low blood sugar! This brings us to an interesting observation. Namely that many people who are depressed or suffering from bipolar depression may have low blood sugar (LBS).

> **Many people who are depressed or suffering from bipolar depression may have low blood sugar**

One theory of LBS is that people who have it crave simple carbohydrates (e.g. sucrose or table sugar) to raise their blood sugar. This works in the short term because the blood sugar is raised quickly. It even brings about a mild kind of high feeling. For a depressed person, this might feel good. However, the drawback comes about an hour later, when the blood sugar crashes down. This happens in response to an over-secretion of insulin that the body sends out to lower the blood sugar level. Such a scenario is common in LBS sufferers.

It is also enlightening to note that alcohol is a fast-acting carbohydrate. According to Krimmel & Krimmel, consumption of alcohol is one of the fastest ways to elevate blood sugar levels. People who drink may be drinking to elevate blood sugar levels. Alcohol gives them a quick fix. Of course that fix only lasts until the pancreas pumps more insulin into the blood and knocks the blood sugar down again.

Those who have ever attended an AA meeting may have noticed all of the sweets that are served. Recovering alcoholics may be trying another ineffective way to raise and stabilize their blood sugar. However, their blood sugar levels are not stabilized. Instead, the same high-low scenario occurs.

John Bradshaw gives us another insight into the cause of high sugar intake. According to Bradshaw, studies show that sugar causes powerful pain-killers to be released by our body chemistry. Large amounts of sugar are being consumed as a pain killer by people who are in psychological pain. Bradshaw views alcohol abuse and alcoholism in a similar way. It's a powerful mood-altering substance to take us out of our pain, so we don't have to feel it.

Prozac has been shown to be very effective in treating depression and other disorders. Supposedly, Prozac has few side-effects compared to older antidepressants. However, it does have side-effects. The side-effects can be found in a book called the *Physicians Desk Reference*.

Prozac is in a class of antidepressants called *selective serotonin-reuptake inhibitors* (SSRI's). This means *Prozac brings about higher levels of active serotonin in the brain by blocking the brain's system that naturally removes serotonin.*

Research has discovered that eating carbohydrates also increases serotonin. Thus, with food we can affect our bio-brain chemistry, too! It should be noted that drugs have a much more potent affect on serotonin levels than eating carbohydrates. But wouldn't it make more sense to eat right and use other *tools* to stay healthy if that is possible.

It seems that there are conflicting opinions, though. Two authors say that carbohydrates contribute to depression (Krimmel & Krimmel). Other research says that carbohydrates may help a depressed person. A closer look shows that the main problem is with *refined carbohydrates.* Both agree on that point. Glucose is fuel for the brain. We need glucose. Sugar (sucrose) turns to glucose, but sucrose can cause problems—depression, etc. What we need are protein and *complex* carbohydrates which give fuel (glucose) to our bodies and brains, but at a slower rate than refined sugars and flours. Refined flour also breaks down and turns to glucose too quickly.

Stress has been linked to both depression and bipolar depression. External circumstances or internal struggles can cause stress.

Most often, stress is caused by a real or imagined threat. When faced with a threatening event we go into what is classically called *the fight or flight response.* When the fight or flight response is evoked, our body's systems react. Our heart rate increases as adrenaline is pumped into our system. Blood pressure increases, and the rate at which our body burns fuel (glucose) increases. If a person suffers from LBS, putting them under stress will increase their cell's rate of burning glucose. This will lower blood sugar and deprive the brain of fuel—glucose. Thus, as mentioned earlier, serotonin level will fall and so will their mood.

A)   Stress affects blood sugar and thus serotonin.

There are also other things that come into play when a human being is under stress. When we are under stress, norepinephrine is secreted. Norepinephrine is another neurotransmitter associated with depression.

B)   Stress causes norepinephrine to be secreted.

Most antidepressants act on one or both of two major neurotransmitters in the brain. Prozac (and other drugs in the same family) affect our serotonin level. The other major classes of antidepressants act on serotonin and norepinephrine. Looking at A) and B) above, we can now see the physiology or biochemistry of sustained and excessive stress depleting *serotonin* and *norepinephrine,* the two major neurotransmitters associated with depression.

This may be one of the reasons why several of the modern forms of therapy that use relaxation and meditation are so effective. Relaxation and meditation give the body time to regenerate the biochemical reserves which have been lost while under stress. Meditation is also a way to *prepare* oneself for the stresses to come. "An ounce of prevention is worth a pound of cure."

- Simple carbohydrates worsen depression
- Stress increases the rate of burning fuel or glucose (blood sugar)
- LBS contributes to depression
- Saturated fats cause sluggishness, slow thinking, and fatigue
- Serotonin affects mood (Serotonin decrease is linked to depression)

- *Prozac affects **serotonin***
- *Other major classes of antidepressants act on **serotonin** and **norepinephrine***
- *Complex carbohydrates increase **serotonin** which boosts our mood*
- *Protein promotes dopamine and **norepinephrine,** which promotes alertness*

From these statements, it is clear to see that there are other ways to affect our mood than taking antidepressants.

Carbohydrates affect serotonin levels, and so our mood. The idea is to keep away from simple carbohydrates like table sugar, candies, cakes, and other foods containing them. Stay away from foods made from processed white bleached flour and white rice. These simple carbohydrates often worsen depression.

Instead, increase complex carbohydrates such as fresh vegetables, baked potatoes, nuts, seeds, beans, brown rice, and whole grain cereals and breads. Fruits are complex carbohydrates and are healthy, too. However, they don't lift one's mood. In addition, too much sweet fruit can affect blood sugar levels in a person with LBS. Accordingly, LBS sufferers should limit sweet fruits.

A basic rule of thumb concerning what we eat is: *the closer to nature the better.* That is, the less the food is processed, the better. The idea is to ingest foods that burn slower, keep blood sugar levels stable and seratonin levels up. Protein takes longer to digest—it is slow-burning, hence good for LBS sufferers. The same is true for most fresh vegetables that are not sweet. Examples of sweet vegetables are: carrots and sweet potatoes.

Dehydration is another factor I believe is linked to depression. Often people who are depressed lack fluid in their bodies. Signs of this are: constant thirst, dark yellow urine, dry or chapped lips, dry skin, constipation, dryness in the nose, and dry eyes.

In order for our body chemistry to work properly we **must** have sufficient fluids. Water is essential to life. Antidepressants and lithium usually alter the body's fluid balances, which may have something to do with their effectiveness.

There is a cyclical nature or a catch-22 situation to depression. A person who is depressed often craves simple carbohydrates (sugar), fat, and stimulants like caffeine. These foods, after giving some temporary relief, may cause a person to become more depressed. When the person is more depressed, he has more of a craving and so on.

Depression > sugar craving > more depression

Stress > worsened LBS > more stress

Stress > depression > more stress > worsened depression

Stress > serotonin and norepinephrine depletion > depression

This appears to be a hopeless scenario. However, there is actually great hope, because a cycle can be broken by removing any element that perpetuates the cycle.

**To break a chain
only one link must be cut**

Without intervention, these cycles often spiral downward. With intervention the spiral can be caused to lead upward. The idea is to gradually replace unhealthy links with healthy ones. Alleviate stress through meditation, rest, and other stress reduction techniques. Improve LBS and neurotransmitter depletion with complex carbohydrates, protein, and other healthy foods. Address depression with therapy and all of the other techniques learned thus far.

These methods will help a person suffering from either depression or euphoria. The most sensible approach is to apply them in a preventive way, before episodes occur.

There is an interesting correlation between my recovery and my diet. I have been predominantly using the cognitive (thought) and feeling approach to healing. But if I were to observe my diet when I was in a severe depression, I would find a real correlation. When I was suffering from severe mood swings, my diet consisted of a lot of sugar and caffeine. At the same time, I was depriving my body of many vitamins that were not in the junk food consumed. For a typical day, my fluid intake consisted of orange juice for breakfast, coke for break, coke for lunch, and another soda with dinner. I drank no plain water. Now, I wonder how my body and mind survived such abuse in the form of sugar and caffeine while lacking the cleansing and purifying action that water gives.

During the time I was going through a deep depression, Ann, a caring girlfriend, did some research on the subject of depression. Ann was into eating healthy foods and believed in good nutrition. When I told her I was taking lithium, Ann expressed concern. Reading some books on depression and nutrition, she learned that there was a correlation between the two. Ann found a doctor who treated people with depression by using nutritional means. I went for a series of blood tests and an all-day glucose tolerance test. I don't remember how many hours it took, but I believe it was 6 or 8. The only thing he found wrong with me was that my blood sugar swings were too great. He said it wasn't diabetes or hypoglycemia, but just that my blood sugar swings too much. He told me to stop eating sugar and gave me a diet I thought I could never follow.

I cut down, but did not stop the sugar—I'm talking mainly about drinks and junk food like donuts and cakes and ice cream. **I had no idea, until I started reading labels, that just about everything the average American eats and drinks has sugar in it.**

At one point, I realized that to a great extent I had conquered my depression and highs using self-help books, talk shows, therapy, cognitive techniques, Codependents Anonymous (CODA) support group, Depressive/Manic-Depressive Support Group (DMDSG), inner child work, and one of the most important tools—meditative prayer.

Years ago my debilitating depressions lasted for several months, then I would be stable for a while. Next, I would slip into a high state of mind. After using the tools mentioned above for a period of years, the depressions and highs all but subsided.

I have had *no deep, long term* depressions since 1987. But every once in a while, I had a *short, but intense* bout with depression. It usually lasted a day or two, sometimes a little longer. It was when I was having one of these in January 1992, that I decided to head for a recovery bookstore and find an answer. *The Low Blood Sugar Handbook* by Krimmel & Krimmel nearly jumped off the shelf at me. I remembered that the night before the shame attack or feeling of depression began, I had indulged in some sweet cakes. Could there be a connection?

I dove into the LBS book with a passion to learn. It provided me with a good understanding of how sugar and caffeine affect the body and the brain! As a result, I went on a no-sugar and no carbohydrate fast. (Carbohydrates turn into sugar in the body). I began to read labels on the food in the grocery store, trying to find products that didn't contain sugar. I began to believe that we Americans are sugar addicts.

Since I have kept my sugar intake low, I have not had an intense depression that I couldn't get myself out of easily. I eat only natural sugars such as in fruits. I even limit fruits and fruit juices if they are sweet. Because grapefruits are not sweet, they are acceptable. I have cut out all refined sugar and almost all products that contain refined sugar, such as soda, cakes, cookies, and so many more unhealthy junk foods.

I want to make a strong suggestion: If you wish to cut out sugar, or go on a sugar and carbohydrate fast, *don't do it without being well-informed.* If possible, use the help of a nutritionist who treats hypoglycemia. If a nutritionist is not affordable, get some good books on the topic and read them. I say this because when I went on the *sugar and carbohydrate* fast, I had severe constipation. Of course there was the good effect of more level blood sugar and stable moods, but the constipation and other side-effects were unpleasant. I felt like a drug addict in withdrawal.

Going on a total sugar and carbohydrate fast as I did may not be a wise idea. However, lowering sugar intake *gradually* may prove to be beneficial. Sugar causes many other problems too—tooth decay, weight gain, and hyperactivity in some people. A friend of mine recently told me of a study which showed that sugar weakens one's immune system, leaving one open to other illnesses.

Something struck me when reading *The Low Blood Sugar Handbook.* The authors state that it is hard to feel or think properly when your blood sugar is kicking you in the brain! This happens because the brain (as well as the eye) has no stored up fuel reserves. Unlike muscles, which can burn fat when energy-deprived, the eye and brain depend on a constant source of glucose in the blood for optimal functioning. That is why some of the first symptoms of low blood sugar are blurred vision, problems with concentration and mood change. The LBS sufferer might not be aware of these symptoms since he or she is so used to having them. Being aware of the symptoms takes practice. This can be helped by a close friend or family member who may notice the signs sooner than the LBS sufferer himself.

A recent study was done on students who had problems concentrating. Each one had their blood sugar tested and *all* were found to be hypoglycemic (when LBS has reached a certain clinical level it is called hypoglycemia).

The following is a dietary comparison from a time period when I had terrible episodes of depression and euphoria to the present, where I no longer have these bouts.

DIET COMPARISON

	Youth (Depression and High Times)	Now
Meat	Much meat	Less meat
Vegetables	Small amount (frozen)	Many (fresh)
Fruit	Almost none	2–3 times a day
Bread	White	Whole wheat or multi-whole grain (at dinner time only)
Potatoes	Fried, baked, french fried, mashed	Baked, microwaved, mashed (at dinner time only)
Pasta	Bleached flour	Artichoke, whole wheat, or spinach flour (dinner time)
Drinks	Orange juice, Coke, 7up, iced tea and hot tea (with lots of sugar), *no plain water*	*Much plain water*, Herb tea, V8, lemon and water, iced herb tea
Salad	Rarely	Once a day or more (with lots of fresh vegetables and protein)
Breakfast	Cereal with sugar, pancakes or french toast with syrup, bacon and eggs	Eggs (1 yolk and the rest egg whites only), grapefruit, squash, cheese & Muesli (no refined sugar)
Dairy	Milk	Plain Yogurt
Snacks	Cookies, ice cream, cake, donuts, potato chips	Nuts, seeds, cheese and celery, fresh fruits and vegetables that contain low carbohydrates.

155

Whenever I drink sweet juice, I water it down. Most of the time I will have three or four parts water to one part juice. Natural juices (no sugar added) cost more, but by the time I water them down, they are less expensive.

The LBS sufferer must eat more often to keep his or her blood sugar stable. In my case, I find that to keep my blood sugar stable I must eat about every 2 to 2-1/2 hours. If I don't, I become tired, irritable, and I get ravenously hungry. It becomes hard to concentrate and my vision gets a little blurry. I've also noticed that I feel cold easily, especially in my extremities (hands and feet). If I eat when I need to, I feel much better. Please understand that there are many possible symptoms. The ones listed are mine; yours may be different. Refer to the LBS book listed in Appendix B for more symptoms. Again, the idea is instead of eating 3 large meals a day, eat 6–8 small meals. In general, it is much healthier to eat several small meals each day instead of a couple of large meals. This is recommended for everyone, not just LBS sufferers. In any event, you can't lose.

Given the evidence, a depressed person would do well to consider the possible connection between their diet and their condition. It is clear that stress and diet play an important role in both the cause and treatment of depression and bipolar depression. **It is a good idea for someone who is in the throes of a major *depression* or *high* to undergo a full battery of physical tests to eliminate the possibility of a physical cause.** I recommend that these tests include an 8-hour glucose tolerance test (GTT). Even further, I recommend that the person eliminate *simple carbohydrates* for 2 weeks to test for glucose intolerance, since it has been found that even GTT's do not always reveal a problem with glucose intolerance or LBS.

At this point I would also like to bring to attention another approach to low blood sugar. It is believed by some that not only simple carbohydrates, but rather *carbohydrates in general,* trigger the insulin reaction and low blood sugar. A simple test for this is: do you get tired easily during the day? Do you get tired after eating a nice pasta meal? Are you sometimes hungry not long after you have eaten a meal with bread or pasta? If so, you might try eating *no* carbohydrates for breakfast or lunch. Snacks shouldn't have carbohydrates either. Since LBS affects people mostly during the daytime, carbohydrates are allowed at dinner time. I have found that this diet gives me much more energy during the day. I get tired far less during the day. It is an easy diet to stay on, since I never have to wait longer than until dinner to eat what I really enjoy—which of course is carbohydrates. A positive side effect of the diet is that I have lost weight with little effort. As with the sugar and carbohydrate fast, constipation is a possible side effect, therefore fiber and plenty of fluids should be consumed to prevent a problem in this area.

It is also advisable to take vitamin supplements daily. B complex is helpful for people who suffer from stress as well as depression. I take a powerful multivitamin with lots of B in it, as well as a supplement of vitamin C and E.

The herb *St. John's Wort* has been found to be a mood enhancer. In Europe, it has long been used as an alternative to antidepressants. Many people find that St. John's Wort alleviates their depression. St. John's Wort is typically used to alleviate mild to moderate depression. The good news about St. John's Wort is that it has minimal side-effects. St. John's Wort may take 4–6 weeks to be effective. One side effect to note is that it can cause a sensitivity to the sun in fair-skinned people. Hence, avoid sun exposure or use sun block. St. John's Wort can be purchased at health food stores. Ask your health food store for other aids to help depression or bipolar depression. They are often an excellent resource for alternatives to drugs.

Dietary control of depression is not a panacea. However, our diet certainly does affect our biochemistry and often does contribute to depression. I believe diet intervention, as well as other methods such as therapy, exercise, support groups, and all of the other tools mentioned thus far should be used in alleviating depression and bipolar depression.

Chapter 9

FAITH

Is Our Faith Making Us Sick or Well?

D oes faith prevent depression and bipolar? No, people of religious faith are not exempt from depression or bipolar. As a matter of fact, several well known Saints and Biblical figures have suffered bouts of severe depression. Some of those were: Elijah and King David of the Old Testament, Saint Francis of Assisi, Saint John of the Cross, and Saint Therese of Lisieux.

Faithful people should expect to go through some darkness. It is often true that one cannot appreciate the light until one has experienced the darkness. Experiencing depression can be indicative of a questioning process—an ultimately healthy, normal occurrence.

Often, it is the pain of our deep depression that causes us to see and change some things that need to be changed about ourselves. Sometimes it helps us to recall things that were done to us that contributed to the cause of our depressions. Childhood abuses repressed by our defense and survival mechanisms might now be surfacing so they can be worked through.

Faith can be helpful in dealing with depression and bipolar depression. However, warped faith can lead to depression, or intensify an existing depression. In my case it did both. The warped view of faith that I had was one of excessive unearned guilt and a fear that God was punishing me for the things I had done wrong. I felt that I was so guilty that God would not forgive me. This obviously intensified my depression and feeling of alienation and hopelessness.

I have since learned that when I do something wrong, it is OK to feel guilty. However, now I go to God and say I'm sorry for what I've done and know He forgives me immediately. Now I am in touch with a loving God, a God who doesn't like it when I sin, but who is *always* yearning to forgive me as He did in the story Jesus told of the Prodigal Son (Luke 15:11-24). He wants us to come right back to Him when we sin, not to run and hide and stay away from Him in fear. I now realize that if I have that kind of terminal guilt, that it is not God who convicts me, but Satan. God always wants me back. As scripture says, "Nothing can separate us from the love of God." (Romans 8:39) So let us not be deceived into thinking that God won't forgive us, for He always will if we just ask Him with a truly repentant heart. He wants so much to forgive us—and to heal us.

Because of my distorted view of faith, I suffered greatly, but I never lost my faith in God. In His mercy and faithfulness, He helped me see the light. Faith, though very painful to me in the past, is what kept me from crumbling to pieces when I was nearing total despair. Faith helped me to fear killing myself when I was contemplating suicide many years ago. Today, my *healthier* faith assists me in staying out of depression. This is accomplished through my intimacy with God in prayer every day and the fellowship I share with believers at church as well. Faith also lifts me out of depressive feelings. If I start to feel depressed, I accept my feelings and then I offer them to God. I share my feelings in support groups and with trusted friends. Often when I take these steps, the depression just melts away.

Saint Francis said, "Praise God in all circumstances."

Faith also brings me to healing and healthy communing with fellow believers. We are all lifted up as we share our struggles with one another and with Christ. Jesus said, "Come to me all you who are burdened and I will give you rest" (Matthew 11.28). We come, and He does give us rest. Thank you, Lord.

Most of the things in this book have dealt with practical methods of overcoming depression and manic depression. I would like to share with you a very personal story of my faith experience. Below is the story of the real Healer. It speaks of the Source of all healing, which is God.

It is through God's Divine Son, Jesus, that I know my healing has come. It is through His mercy and the showering of His grace that I have been healed. At times, during meditative prayer, He has touched me in a direct way. As I was praying, or just sitting and *being* with God, with Jesus, suddenly I felt waves of His grace penetrating my being. Tears filled my eyes

160

and poured down my cheeks like a warm healing rain. I felt so unworthy, so thankful, so peaceful. I knew it could only be Jesus. These were not tears of wailing, or sympathy, or sadness. They were a different kind of tears. I call them healing tears, drops from heaven washing my soul and healing my heart. My only response was, Lord I am not worthy. But thank you, thank you. And then I felt as if He was saying, just "be still and know that I am God." I am thankful to You, Oh God, for it is You who has broken my chains and set me free. Forever I will Praise Your Name!

This experience was so healing for me, but it was not a miracle cure that was complete and an end in itself. To this day, I have experienced many times like this. The healing for me is ongoing, and He continues to touch me in His presence.

There were many times when I was younger that I felt like I was beginning to get depressed and I prayed, yet I still got depressed. The deeper levels of healing that I have mentioned started only when I mustered up the courage to begin opening up in counseling—sharing my deepest hurts and fears. When we open up in counseling, we open ourselves to God and the ways He heals us through our brothers and sisters of humanity. At that time, I also began a time of meditative prayer every day. I did this because a friend of mine from India had told me, "There are really only two paths to God, Love and Devotion." All other paths lead to these two. I didn't know if I could love properly, but I knew I could be devoted, so I began a time of daily devotion to God.

With a single candle lit (which helps to focus and center myself), I put on John Michael Talbot's tape called *Quiet Reflections* or another favorite—*Heart of the Shepherd*. The Spirit has touched me deeply through Talbot's music. *Quiet Reflections* has words to it. There is another tape called *Empty Canvas*, an instrumental that is excellent for meditation.

The simple decision to begin a daily devotional time has changed my life immensely. Spending time alone with God has opened a door to the abundant Grace He longs to shower us with. Developing a personal relationship with Jesus Christ as Friend, Lord, Teacher, Counselor and Shepherd has flooded my life with healing.

> He will be called,
> Wonderful Counselor, Mighty
> God.
> Everlasting Father, Prince of
> Peace.   Isaiah 9:6

161

Something else that I did was to ask all of my Christian friends to pray for me. Prayer is powerful! It sometimes takes time to work, but it works. Thank you everyone who has prayed for me.

Thoughts on prayer

There are many ways to pray: Some say formal prayers; others just talk to God like a Father, telling him their hurts, wants, needs, and joys. We can just sit and listen. Some say a mantra (repeating a word or phrase over and over, maybe a scripture). Some read scripture as prayer. Others sing, a beautiful way to pray! Some actions we might take during prayer are *Confession, Petition, Intercession, Thanksgiving, and Praise*: In confession of course, we confess our sins to God and ask His forgiveness. Petition is what most of us do. We ask God for what we want. We ask Him to help us do something or get something for ourselves. Intercessory prayer is praying for another's well being, health, happiness, etc. Thanksgiving is thanking God for what He has given us. Praise is when we worship God for who He is. I've heard some say that prayer is simply spending time with God.

There is another type of prayer that I have found to be very powerful in my life. It is *prayer of trust*. Lord, no matter what happens, I trust that it will be for my highest good. I trust you, Oh Lord God. When life has brought me pain and suffering in my past, I now see how you have used it to teach me and to help me grow. This experience has helped me to understand suffering and the reason for it. Suffering teaches us, if we are open to its lessons. Suffering makes us grow in ways that we might never have dreamed. When we suffer for love, we shine! Job in the old testament said about God, "Though He slay me, yet will I trust Him." Wow. What faith. What trust. What acceptance. Can you see the freedom that such an attitude brings? "Though He slay me, yet will I trust Him." If we no longer fear suffering or death, what else is there to fear? What, then, can bind us?

> **When we suffer for love, we shine!**

It seems that so often when we pray, we despair and give up. We think, why am I praying when I never get an answer to my prayers? There is an encouraging story in the Bible concerning persistence in prayer:

Then Jesus told his disciples a parable to show them that they should always pray and not give up. He said: "In a certain town there was a judge who neither feared God nor cared about men.

162

And there was a widow in that town who kept coming to him with the plea, 'Grant me justice against my adversary.'"

"For some time he refused. But finally he said to himself, 'Even though I don't fear God or care about men, yet because this widow keeps bothering me, I will see that she gets justice, so that she won't eventually wear me out with her coming!'"

And the Lord said, "Listen to what the unjust judge says. And will not God bring about justice for his chosen ones, who cry out to him day and night? Will he keep putting them off? I tell you, he will see that they get justice, and quickly..." Luke 18:1-8

Something about that parable really got to me. It was when the Lord said, "he will see that they get justice, *and quickly...*" The Lord doesn't always answer us right away. However, if we are persistent, if we never give up, He will answer us, *and quickly*, but at the time He chooses. This has happened in my life. I testify that if we persist in faith and in prayer, God will answer us. He will reward our faith. He has rewarded mine, sometimes after praying for many years. I trust He will yours!

Thoughts on Faith

To have faith is to be sure of the things we hope for,
To be certain of the things we cannot see.

The Bible - Hebrews 11:1

Faith is knowing that the rope will hold the swing up
without understanding the Physics of why.

Faith is an act of belief
where there is no tangible proof.

Too often faith happens when all of our attempts fail
in despair we cry out to God
and He helps us

163

One of the things that I love about the Christian faith is its simplicity. The whole Bible and our duties as Christians can be summed up in two commands:

1. Love the Lord your God with all your heart and with all your soul and with all your mind.

2. Love your neighbor as yourself.

Matthew 22:37–40

In order to follow those commands we must know what love is. I believe that the word *love* has been twisted and distorted by some people's selfish desires over the ages, or in many cases it has been just plain misunderstood.

Balance has been built into the second commandment. However, that balance has been shaken. It has been shaken by some peoples' misinterpretation of the commandment's meaning. Still others deliberately misinterpret it for their own selfish end.

First of all, I have learned that I must prioritize things properly, just as Jesus did. God must come first, above everyone and everything. That includes our parents, all other authority figures, our girlfriends, our wives, our children, and ourselves. God must be our first and strongest desire. If He is not, we will suffer, or at least not live life to the fullest, receiving the immeasurable joys that He promises us (both in this world and eternally). My life, my choices, and the "results" of seeking Him first are proof to me that this way, HIS WAY, works. He has given me joy, peace and hope that I never believed were possible.

Probably three of the most important things I was ever encouraged to do are: 1) to invite Jesus into my heart and my life 2) to begin a personal relationship with Him, praying and talking with Him on a daily and even moment by moment basis and 3) to spend regular time reading the Bible to learn about Him and God's will for me and my life. I firmly believe that it is only the Lord who could have guided me out of the *maze* of family, societal and religious dysfunction that I was in. That is why He is called Shepherd, Teacher, Healer and Wonderful Counselor. I also call Him my best friend.

"Love" What is it? What is it not?

First I will start off with sharing what I believe *love is not*. These are typical impostors of love:

- Doing things out of duty, when we really resent doing them

- Doing things to avoid feeling guilty if we don't do them

- Jealousy is not a sign of love

- Love is not proud

- Manipulation is not love

- Being demanding is not love

- Trying to make someone feel guilty is not love

- Giving, *with strings attached*—looking for something back—is not love

- Parents demanding children to respect them, when they are not respecting their children, is not love

- It is not love to try to make someone into what we want them to be, instead of nurturing and encouraging them to be who they are, which is what God intended them to be

- Selflessness for the wrong reasons (for instance, *to look good*), is not love

Love is:

◊　Outgoing

◊　Not looking so much to get, as to give

◊　Giving little, if giving little is all I can give without looking for a payback or without feeling resentful

◊　Willing and able to suffer for the person loved, if circumstances demand it. However, love does not seek to suffer

Kind

                        Gentle

          Freeing   Patient

                  Humble

Genuine   Forgiving

          Taking care of oneself as well as others

          Mutual respect

This leads to the second commandment and how it has been distorted and imbalanced by much of our religious teachings. Often in our churches we hear our preachers say: "Don't be selfish. Go out and give to your neighbor. Take care of your neighbor." However, Jesus said, "Love your neighbor as yourself." See the balance? I may add for clarity: "Love your neighbor as yourself;" neither more, nor less.

If we only love ourselves and not our neighbor, we are not keeping the command. Likewise, if we only love our neighbor and are not loving ourselves, we are not keeping the commandment. Some would say that it is not possible to love another if we don't love ourselves. I agree.

Is it selfish to take care of myself? Let us substitute the words "take care of" for the word "love" in the second commandment. "Take care of" your neighbor as you "take care of" yourself. If I go to help my neighbor clean his or her house when mine is filthy, then go home and have no time to clean my own house, won't I feel a little resentful? Won't my resentment grow, especially if this is a constant habit? Whereas, if I keep my house nice and clean, I see that it feels good to do that. Since I feel good, I want to share that good feeling, that love, with my neighbor. As a result, I go and help him or her out of charity, sharing the goodness, the love that I feel for myself.

Some people fall into a trap, myself included. It is this: I know that I am hurting. I am beyond my limit of giving generously and in charity. I may even feel resentful that I am not being loved back by the one or ones to whom I am giving, but I feel so torn by my *responsibility* to love them. Who will love them if I don't? [TRAP]. We think there is no one who will do it but us. We think we are the only one loving them. In short, we are playing god! Won't God provide? Where is our faith in Him who watches over all? It is hard to let go. But we must, in an act of faith and trust, *let go and let God*. It should also be considered that sometimes God allows people to suffer in order to give them a strong call to a change of heart. If we get in the way of God's disciplining them, we open ourselves to His discipline. God's discipline can be painful! It is similar to a loving parent who disciplines their child with a spanking. Keep in mind that this type of thinking should not be used to avoid helping when helping would be the loving thing to do. The right thing to do can be discerned by using wisdom, prayer and seeking counsel.

A Catholic nun friend of mine once said to me, "Paul, can you imagine what it would be like if we really did love our neighbor as we love ourselves?" Consider what a poor job some of us do in taking care of ourselves. Imagine if we treated our neighbor the way we treat ourselves. How can we give what we don't have? We must love ourselves and let others love us (and of course, and most of all, let God love us). Then, we will have the energy to go out and love others. The best is to care for both ourselves and our neighbor in an equal way.

"Love the Lord your God
with all your heart,
and with all your soul,
and with all your mind."

"Love your neighbor as yourself"

Matthew 22:37-39

167

Chapter 10

MY RECOVERY

The Major Events

T he following is an outline of the story of my recovery from a disease with the behavioral symptoms of manic depression, currently called bipolar affective disorder. Taking a similar path, or at least a path with similar healing elements in it could bring a depressed or bipolar depressed person from the darkness of despair into the healing light of hope.

> **Full recovery is a life-long process. The important thing is to be on the road, and to know how to steer, to know how to bring ourselves back in control if we slip out.**

The major factors that I see in my recovery are the following:

1. I did not accept the label that I was a manic depressive and that I had to take pills for the rest of my life to be OK.

2. I realized there was something wrong and that I needed help to beat it—I overcame denial.

3. I constantly sought answers to the way I felt and what I could do to feel better. Self-help books, talk shows, articles, seminars and authorities in the field of recovery were some of my sources.

4. A major breakthrough happened during and after my last major depression, which was in the fall of 1987. I'll elaborate a bit:

In all of my previous depressions, I never told anyone how I really felt. This time, while I was in the midst of a depression, *I decided to tell Judy, my therapist.* I was afraid, but with the help of Judy, *who provided a safe place,* I mustered up the *courage* to open up. Judy *was a therapist who didn't judge me,* (not even in her expressions) as I told her the things that I deeply feared so much. This is where the healing really began. It began when I stopped hiding what I was thinking and feeling. Instead, *I opened up* and shared.

I started to feel better when I was in the middle of a depression! This never happened before. Judy *compassionately listened* to me without judging. *She accepted me.* I felt that *Judy believed in me.* She had faith in me, that I wasn't a "manic depressive."

We both agreed that I had a predisposition to manic depressive–type behavior when put under enough stress. I had no problem with that. It is much better to *have behavior* than to *be something* negative. *I can change my behavior.* I cannot change my *being*—what or who "I am." I don't like labels. It was true, I did have the typical behavior. Everybody has their Achilles Heel. *If put under enough stress for long enough, anyone will break down.* It's just a matter of which way. Some get depressed, some get heart attacks, some get ulcers, some get strokes, and I could go on. Bipolar behavior was my body and mind's way of coping with what I now know was some pretty severe hurts I was dealing with.

Judy also helped me to *release guilt* that I was feeling at the time. My sense of guilt was related to my parents who were in need, but had few friends to help them because they alienated people from their life. She helped me to see that it was not my fault and encouraged me to live my life. This release of guilt empowered me to *decide* if I really wanted to be there for my Dad, who was dying of cancer, out of love rather than out of guilt. I chose to be there, out of love more than duty. Consequently, I have a great peace about his death.

Judy also taught me some *tools* to be able to use in dealing with the paranoia I felt, which was quite severe and intensified the depression immeasurably. I thank you Judy, from the bottom of my heart for all you have done for me.

Most of the terms above that are in *italics* are elements which I believe are powerful in the healing process. In this form they are very easy to pick out and use.

5. MEDITATIVE PRAYER. While seeing Judy, I also began a time of meditative prayer nearly every day. This was very powerful in my healing, and I still do this nearly every day. My prayer consisted of sitting in quiet with God, listening to John Michael Talbot and other Christian tapes, praying for my enemies as Jesus taught, a time of singing songs of thanks and praise to God (Taize Chants), and asking God to bless all of my friends, myself and my family. Praying for my enemies is the hardest thing, but has brought about such healing in me. "Enemies" are people whom I feel have hurt me. For a person suffering from paranoia, that can be many different people. Prayer has helped me get out of my sometimes obsessive thinking and my paranoid thinking. Prayer time is also a de-stressing time of relaxation and rest.

6. WILL TRAINING. Because I had an extremely critical father, I have many thousands of hours of critical tapes in my head. I have learned that this kind of critical thinking was much the cause of my depressions. Depression is anger (judgment or criticism) turned inward. I have learned to a great degree to be aware of when my obsessive critic is taking control. At this point I fill my mind with prayer, or songs of non-fear. This helps to wash away the critical thoughts by replacing them with peaceful and joyful thoughts and songs. I also read positive wholesome material, listen to edifying music, watch wholesome movies and spend time with healthy people. All of this positive input helps my brain to have a lot of wholesome tapes to access and process rather than just the old critical material from childhood.

7. FEELING. I have learned how to feel my feelings, such as anger. To feel it and to ask what it is trying to tell me. Sometimes the anger is "just" and telling me to confront someone. At other times my anger is far more intense than the situation warrants. The circumstances may be touching on my baggage (past hurt) and so I let the anger go. I let it go by writing it down, talking about it with a trusted friend or therapist and by praying about it. This is not easy. It takes immense discipline. However, the peace that comes after the anger is let go far outweighs the cost.

8. DEPRESSIVE / MANIC DEPRESSIVE SUPPORT GROUP (DMDSG). At DMDSG I received empathy from others who felt like I felt. Consequently, I did not feel so alone. I also got information about some of the medications I took at that time. This group was a necessary and good step in my recovery. However, this group mainly seemed to see medication as the answer. After I attended a Codependents Anonymous (CODA) group a few times and returned to DMDSG, I saw that the structure of the DMDSG meetings was not as well rounded as CODA meetings. CODA meetings did not advocate drug therapy. Rather, CODA encouraged people to work

through their emotional issues. Hence, I discontinued DMDSG meetings and moved on to CODA meetings. See Appendix "A" to find a support group.

9. CODA. Codependents Anonymous, a 12-step recovery program which has branched off from the highly successful 12-step group AA (Alcoholics Anonymous), is structured to be a safe place and a healing environment. I have received so much support, non-shaming faces, detached compassion, and new information from CODA. I highly recommend it. I still attend CODA meetings and continue to grow in this nurturing environment. (See Appendix C to learn more about Codependence and CODA.)

10. THE FAMILY SYSTEM. I have studied John Bradshaw's video tape called "Bradshaw On: The Family." The family is shown as a system. Bradshaw explains how family dysfunction is set up and how it is perpetuated. The view is no longer to focus only on the *identified patient*, (like the depressive or manic depressive) who needs help, but on the whole family as a system. The family dynamic is often what causes a person to get depressed or addicted. If not, it is often what permits and perpetuates the dysfunctional behavior. I couldn't recommend this tape highly enough to someone who is dealing with depression, manic depression, addiction, or a host of other struggles.

11. INNER CHILD WORK. Inner child work is another method of healing which involves getting in touch with childhood memories and grieving memories which we may not have been allowed to grieve, yet which help perpetuate our dysfunctional behavioral patterns. I have participated in one of John Bradshaw's *Healing our inner child* workshops. Workshops of this kind can accelerate the healing process.

12. STAY CONNECTED. Staying connected to a core group of friends, my family, my church community and my men's group brings me wonderful support and joy. Having a *special lady* (my wife) and her family in my life has been the icing on the cake. *Love, true love, is the most powerful healing medicine that there is.* My love gives that to me and I give it to her. Nobody does it better than my love.

Reasons why I don't fear getting chronically depressed again:

I understand where I came from:

First of all, I don't fear the thought of possible recurrence of my depressions and euphoria because *I understand now why I suffered from depression and euphoria.* It began in my childhood as emotional or mental illnesses often do. I had an extremely critical and domineering father who also had emotional problems and was diagnosed schizophrenic when that was the catch-all diagnosis. When my father was sick with his illness and away in the hospital, I experienced abandonment. I also experienced the lack of the presence of a nurturing father during that time. My father suffered from paranoid thoughts which he passed on to me. I loved my father and it is difficult to write what I am writing. However, it is a must in the healing process. I need to understand what happened to me, allow myself to feel the feelings I have about what happened to me, and then forgive and let it go. I also write so that you, the reader, might begin to understand and face your particular problems. Hopefully you will write them down, feel your feelings about them, forgive the offender and heal also.

My father gave me a lot of love, too. There are so many things which I am grateful to my father for. Little things which he has taught me and given me are so special to remember, especially since he has passed on. He really tried to love and at times we did connect. I cherish those memories. Thanks Dad.

There were many dysfunctional ways of thinking and behavior in my family of origin. Some that I have uncovered are: Anger mismanagement, sarcasm, *control through guilt, fear and abandonment*, denial, pride, shame, destructive teasing, put downs, discounting accomplishments and kindness; feeling our feelings was discouraged (especially anger), and *children were made to feel responsible for the parent's feelings.* Others were: children were made to feel powerless in a parent-run home, manipulation, withholding of praise, blaming, digs and perfectionism (which leaves out God).

Sometimes anger was held in and then acted out in covert and harmful ways—after which the person would deny any accusations that they did anything harmful. Or they would instigate anger and then deny that they did anything wrong! Talk about crazy-making! I believe that this is far more damaging than overt control and abuse. At least with overt control and abuse, a person can respond with anger to defend him or herself. I felt as though I was raped of my anger. How could I be angry at a person who didn't do anything? Even more crazy making was that they really believed they didn't do anything! The pain was felt, but how could a person strike back at someone who *apparently* was so innocent? That person denied instigating conflict, and they seemed sincere. Yet the arrow struck the heart.

> **The person denied instigating conflict, and they seemed sincere. Yet the arrow struck the heart.**

When my pain was too great to hold in anymore, my anger poured out like a dam breaking. I was **diagnosed** as a *manic depressive* by a psychiatrist who only took notice of my symptoms and neglected to look for what might have been fueling them. So when I became angry, my parents could accuse me of being manic. And surely they were right because even the doctors agreed with them! Do you think that accusation calmed me down? You're right, it angered me even more. Now I was really manic—according to my parents. They said I should take my medication. *In retrospect it seems that they would rather keep me medicated than to look at how they fit into the problem.* Surely the problem was me, not them! Here I was so hurt, so filled with pain and anger. Instead of looking for a cause of the anger, I was now *labeled* which only increased my hurt, self-doubt and anger. This deepened my parents' denial which further increased my pain. I was pushed to the limits of my sanity by what was happening. *So they say you're crazy.* Beware, before you believe it! Take a good look at the ones who are telling you that you're crazy or sick. The problem was really in our *family system* which involved myself as well as my parents and siblings. We had severe relational dysfunctions. Because communication methods were extremely unhealthy, I have had to learn more functional ways of communicating. These new and more healthy ways of communicating have shown their fruit in my friendships. These friendships are functional. They are mutually beneficial, supportive and encouraging.

In retrospect, I realize that I had emotionally immature parents. Perfectionism was also a problem. Our parents were good Catholics trying to bring up their children to be *perfect*, moral, flawless, and obedient children. What they neglected to see is that in trying to make me what they believed was a *good* child, they rejected who I really was. Being crazy has a lot to do with trying to be who you are not. So it's no wonder I am a little crazy! A parent says you should be *this*. But I am me, not *this*. But my parent must be right. So there must be something wrong with me. This is the way a child thinks.

As I looked at my parents a little closer, I saw that there was a real problem with suppression of anger, holding onto anger or hate, and a lack of forgiveness and humility. When people have traits like these and don't deal with them through introspection and/or counseling, they only pass them on to their children. What a package we children had to deal with between Mom and Dad's unresolved emotional issues and negative traits. No doubt that they received a lot of these dysfunctions from their parents and their societal conditioning. Knowing this helps me to forgive them.

The beauty is that Mom is continually working on her issues. I also continue to work on mine. We have a more healthy, happy relationship of mutual respect and caring now than we have ever had.

We cannot change our family members, we really can't change anyone else. We can only change ourselves. So we must seek to change ourselves. However, as a person changes, then any relationship which they are in changes because they are a part of that relationship. As we heal ourselves, we will see that it is like a pebble which is dropped into a still pond.

> **As surely as the ripples from that pebble go out and touch every side of the pond, so do the ripples of our lives go out and touch all other lives.**

Now let's rap up where I came from. As a child I was not only *not allowed* to be myself at home, but I also remember being laughed at and put down at the school which I attended. This is oppression. Remember *oppression leads to anger and depression.*

Both of my parents were emotionally immature and too needy themselves to give me what I needed to grow as a healthy child. School children reinforced the *it's not OK to be me* attitude. Thus, I was not *me* for a long time.

At the age of fifteen, my parents got divorced. I recall quite vividly my reaction to the divorce. I felt numb, emotionally numb. When a friend asked about it, it was as though I had no feelings about it. Save for several times, I remember coming home from school to an empty house and missing Mom. I also recall writing my mother a letter and crying as I wrote it and asked her to come home. She replied with a no. It hurt tremendously then, but now I understand that she obviously moved out for a reason.

Recently I heard a talk show which said that major symptoms from divorce don't show up until five years after the divorce. That was precisely the time when I had my first very serious depression.

The things mentioned above, in addition to several things stated in the CAUSES chapter and others woven throughout this book were clearly the causes for my depressions and bipolar swings. Of course, the causes were not only external. As mentioned earlier in this book, at one point I had to stop *blaming*, pick up my baggage and walk. Healing involved changing *my own* dysfunctional attitudes, thinking, and behavior. Wherever they came from, they were mine now and it was up to me to change them.

**At one point I chose to stop *blaming*,
and pick up my baggage and walk.**

**Healing involved changing *my own* dysfunctional
attitudes, thinking, and behavior.**

I know where I am at:

That was then and this is now. Now I can be who I am. It feels so good just to be who I am. It also feels good to forgive. Though it has been (and still is) hard work to forgive, I know I *must* in order to heal and stay healthy.

I have a good support network, just in case I feel the dark cloud of depression coming over me again. Even more importantly though, I perform preventive maintenance work which keeps me out of depression and highs.

This is accomplished through daily meditative prayer, attending support groups when I need to, keeping my stress level at its optimum but carefully avoiding excessive stress, and keeping balance in the following areas of my life: social, emotional, intellectual, spiritual, and physical.

Using the TOOLS in the chapter so titled, gives me great strength to keep out of depression. Many of these tools have become habitual, which for me is the goal—to do them without thinking about it too much. I also make it a habit to hang around people who don't try and oppress me but rather encourage me to express "me." I allow myself to feel my feelings and express them, including, and especially, anger. I attempt to do this in assertive rather than aggressive ways. I have friends I can trust and who trust me. These special people accept me as I am and I accept them for who they are. I love them. And they love me.

Having changed my diet to get off the sugar and caffeine roller coaster also helps keep me out of depression. Finally, I am pursuing my dream and not doing what someone else thinks I should do (be it relatives or society). To nurture my dreams, I make it a point to hang around people who support and encourage my pursuit of them.

All of these things together with so many others mentioned throughout this book, including bringing the message which I have received about conquering depression and bipolar depression to others, leaves little room for me to get depressed again. *Ultimately, my trust is in God who has saved me and I trust will keep me safe.*

Some thoughts and quotes

*We must be the master of our feelings
focus and direct the energy we get from them
toward accomplishing good
and toward the healing of ourselves and others.*

Children are people. They may be little people, but they are people, not possessions.

177

We don't own our children. They belong to God. We have the awesome responsibility of loving and caring for them.

*Children, respect your parents and
parents, respect your children!*

*If you say you love me, but you don't respect me
and treat me well, I have trouble believing you.*

Admission of weakness is the beginning of strength.

*Control is not Love (although we often confuse the two).
Love is a freeing experience.*

Love is giving, not only looking to get.

Healthy "relationship love" goes both ways.

*A loving person is willing to suffer for the person they love.
(Healthy suffering, not the sick type.)*

Love is gentle and love is kind.

Love is accepting and love is challenging.

    In loving another, it is wise to be mostly accepting and occasionally challenging—maybe 90% to 10%. Of course this ratio is highly dependent on circumstances and on the unique individuals involved.

Love is not driven by guilt.

Love is challenging someone who is hurting me.

Love is a decision.

Love does not demand its own way.

Love takes care of both self and neighbor.

Love is putting God first.

God is love.

Love is giving honestly, the little we can.

Love is not giving you what you want,
if it is more than I can give charitably.

179

A loving person can get angry.

*Because I am angry at you does not mean
I don't love you.*

A loving person seeks to forgive (and does).

Forgiveness often takes time and work to achieve.

To forgive, I need God's help.

*A loving relationship involves
mutual respect, commitment, and caring.*

Jealousy is not love.

The flip side of freedom is responsibility.

*If a person's freedom allows them to carelessly step all over
someone else, I would rather not be around such a person.*

To change with change can lower stress

Often we think that it is most comfortable to be still and not change
ourselves or our lives. But if everything around us is changing and we try to

remain still, it would be like trying to hold a raft still in a raging river. Which takes more work, to stay still or to go with the flow?

With regard to changing with change, I speak of technology, computers, etc., benign things. However, if the change involves our values and the river is flowing in the direction of subverting good values, maybe it is time to dig the anchor in *deep*. Subverting good values can cause a person an incredible amount of stress, eventually leading to depression and physical sickness. Accordingly, to go in the direction of more pure values can lead us to happiness and health.

SOME AFFIRMATIONS I USE

1. When I feel someone said something deliberately to hurt or belittle me, when I feel that someone is attacking my weak points, I pray:

> Dear God, I don't find that You convict me for my weakness. I hurt from what this person said, but oh God, it is You who I need approval from. It is You who I get my esteem from. I will not put this person as a "god" by letting what he or she thinks of me affect the way I feel to such a great degree. Thank You Lord, now I have peace.

2. If tempted to lust, I remind myself:

> I am aware that pursuing these thoughts harms me, and maybe the other person too—on some level. I realize lust is detrimental to any association we might have.

> So I say to myself, "Peace be with you." or, "God bless you. I know you are really a spirit and a valuable human being and not just an object of lust." In this way, a feeling of lust is turned into a prayer.

3. If I find myself judging or belittling another person (whether in my mind or out loud):

> I stop myself and say, "I'm OK, you're OK. I'm no better than you. You are no better than me. I wish you peace."

181

4. If I find myself feeling inferior to another or belittling myself, I stop myself and say:

> I'm OK, you're OK. I have my weaknesses and so do you. You have gifts that I may not have. I see that you are good at them. I have gifts that you don't have and I am good at them. Let us not compete. There is no sense in that. Let us both admire each other's gifts. Let us use them to help one another.

5. When I start to feel proud, I remind myself:

> "Jesus, You are the vine. I am a branch. Cut off from You, I will die. But living in You I will bear much fruit. You Oh Lord are the source of my esteem and my worth." (John 15: 1-4)

6. When I have emotions that are overwhelming me, when I have obsessive thoughts, or when I am trying to love unconditionally, which I just can't seem to do without help, I say to myself:

> I trust God
> and ask for His help
> in *all* that I do.
>
> I can only
> truly love
> with God's help.
>
> I realize that
> I cannot do it alone.
> Please help me Lord.

7. When I am feeling angry or rejected, I say:

> I am not attached to suffering.
> I am not attached to what I feel angry at.
> I am not attached to my anger.
> So
> **I will let go of all of these**
> and accept what is.

LABELING

LABELING LEAVES NO ROOM FOR GROWTH.

LABELING STEALS THE HEART OF "HOPE."

It leaves no room for "change" and moving into a different space. Life is change, "Life is Growth"

NOT TO CHANGE

NOT TO GROW

FOR ME

IS EQUIVALENT TO DEATH

To allow someone to LABEL me Manic Depressive is to put the chains on again. It is to take my freedom away. To smother me.

I CHOOSE "LIFE"!

I CHOOSE GROWTH!

*I accept no labels which lock me in and don't allow for growth, **for life**.*

I was once diagnosed as a manic depressive. I had all of the behavior that went with that harsh LABEL. I never accepted that LABEL. I did accept that my thoughts and behavior hurt both myself and others and needed to be changed. They have been changed. Much inner hurt had to be healed. It has been. My life had to change. It has, and still is changing. My thinking had to change. It has changed and still is changing. Yes, once I had the "behavioral symptoms" of what some people call manic depression.

I HAVE GROWN!

and today

I AM

MANIC

DEPRESSIVE

NO

MORE!

In conclusion, I would like to say at this point that I am thankful for having gone through the living hell which I endured. I wouldn't want to go through it again, but I am thankful because this is what made me who I am today. I like myself as I am. I am also thankful, because it has helped me to feel the suffering of my brothers and sisters of humanity. I can empathize with others who suffer, and hopefully relieve some of the unnecessary pain many people endure. My trials have been the fuel for this book, which I hope helps at least one other person undergoing similar trials. Then it will be worth the time spent writing it.

Actually, it is already worth it. Writing this book has brought me to another area of healing. Getting it all out, in a logical readable order, has helped me to affirm and believe in my own healing *process*.

I believe that when we use our painful experiences to try and help others, it makes that experience useful and valuable, not just a hellish time we want to forget. Rather, that experience is now a source of strength and joy. All I have to do is think of how I was when I was so depressed, compared to how I am now, and I feel so joyful and happy just to be out of that. A pit of despair has been turned into an endless *well* of joy which can be drawn from with just a thought. What a treat! A treat, and a **hope** I wish to offer all of my readers who may be going through the fire as they read this.

Now I have purpose in life, a reason to live. Now there is joy in my life which I couldn't have had any other way. There is hope for the future. I wish for all of you, my brothers and sisters, hope, healing, joy, and peace. But most of all, I wish you love. For

Love is the reason we are all here.

SELF-HELP PHONE NUMBERS AND SUPPORT GROUPS

Please note that addresses and numbers do change. Use directory assistance or library sources to obtain current ones if a number is no longer correct.

Emergency 911
Suicide Prevention Hotline (For NJ and some other areas).800–272–4630
Self-Help Clearinghouse, Denville, NJ (outside of NJ) 973–625–7101
    (inside NJ only)..800–367–6274
Depressed Anonymous (National 12 step program)............502–969–3359
Codependents Anonymous National 602–277–7991
    (will find a CODA group in your area)
Codependents Anonymous...602–468–1149
    for people in helping professions
    (to find a local CODA group)
National Support Group ACOA...310–534–1815
    (Adult Children of Alcoholics)
Mood Disorder Support Group (focus is manic dep.).........212–533–MDSG
National Empowerment Center (NEC) ....800–POWER 2 U
    An excellent source of information for people into
    self empowerment and self-healing vs. institutional.
    A slogan of theirs "Labels belong on jars not people"
National Depressive/Manic Depressive Association...........800–826–3632
    (NDMDA) (Focus is on a Drug approach
    toward coping with manic depression)
New Life Treatment Centers 800–NEW–LIFE
    (Christian Counseling)
National Clearinghouse for Alcohol & Drug Information...800–729–6686

Childhelp USA Child Abuse Hotline 800–422–4453
National Aids Information Clearinghouse.........................800–458–5231
National Information and Referral Service 800–531–5305
(I found these people to be very helpful.)

Sierra Tucson Treatment Center, Arizona.........................800–842–4487
        Depression, Manic Depression, Addictions, etc.

Cottonwood Treatment Center, Arizona ....800–877–4520 or
        Depression, Manic Depression, Addictions, etc   888–843–0618

The Meadows, Wickenberg, Arizona (Pia Melody)............800–621–4062 or
        Depression, Manic Depression, Addictions, etc.   800–632–3697

Generally Addiction Treatment Centers use many healthy methods of treatment and are well rounded in their treatment plan (e.g. counseling, group therapy, art therapy, life skills training, grief work, family of origin evaluation, and work). I highly recommend these!

Resource on Cognitive Therapy:
WEB site—www.FeelingGood.com
Contains links to find cognitive therapists around the country.

NARSAD
(National Alliance for Research on Depression and Schizophrenia)
208 South LaSalle Street, Suite 1428
Chicago, IL 60604–1003
312–641–1666

Depressive and Manic Depressive Association (DMDA National)
730 North Franklin
Box 3395
Chicago, IL 60654
800–826–3632 (Note that this group is drug-oriented in its approach)

NAMI
(Manic Depressive National Alliance for Mentally Ill)
1901 North Ft. Meyer Drive, Suite 5000
Arlington, VA 22209–1604
703–524–7600

Appendix B

INFORMATION SOURCES

Self-Help Books, Videos, and Audio Tapes

<u>Videos</u>

Bradshaw On: The Family
    by John Bradshaw
    To order this video call 713–529–9437
    It may be available in bookstores too.

        Bradshaw explains the family as a system. He addresses depression, addiction to drugs, sex, work, alcohol, food, and much more. He also deals with other mental illnesses. Bradshaw cites not only the causes of addiction and mental illness, but he offers HOPE. He describes the road to healing using methods that are very clear and easy to understand. This is also in book form. The video is much more graphic, clear, and interesting. The video is expensive, but excellent. Ask your library to get it if they don't already have it. Bradshaw is on many public television channels. This video has helped me to make sense out of the craziness that I have lived in and helped me to understand some of the apparently crazy feelings I have felt. Bradshaw has several other excellent videos also.

Boundaries
>by Dr. Henry Cloud and Dr. John Townsend
>To order this video call: 800-676-HOPE
>>Drs. Cloud and Townsend are simply excellent. This video series is a must see for the depression or bipolar sufferer as well as for family members of sufferers. If you cannot afford the videos, I highly recommend that you ask your library to purchase them, or that you at least read the book of the same title listed on one of the following pages. I have found all of their work excellent and well balanced.

Audio Tapes

Inner Talk for a Confident Day
>by Susan Jeffers, Ph.D 1990
>>Susan Jeffers is author of *Feel the Fear & Do It Anyway*. This is a tape of her *daily affirmations*. It is excellent, especially for those of us that have thousands of hours of critical parent tapes in our head. This tape helps put some good stuff in our heads. Remember, good thoughts usually precipitate good feelings.

Stress Busters
Using the Mind to Relax the Body
>Rodale Books, Emmaus, PA 18098
>>This tape is a must. It uses two of the most widely used methods of relaxation, *Progressive Relaxation* and *Autogenic Training*. These methods work! Remember, when we relax our bodies our biochemistry balances itself. Since *stress* is the number one trigger for depression and bipolar depression, we must find ways to relax daily.

What I Believe/Deep Relaxation
>by Louise L. Hay, 1983
>>An excellent relaxation tape. I don't agree with some of her "What I believe" side, but the relaxation side is excellent for de-stressing. Deep relaxation helps the body to correct its chemical imbalances.

Focus On The Family tape series call 1–800–AFAMILY
>A good tape is:
>"Getting Married, It's more than saying I DO." This Tape is actually for singles who want to know what to look for in a mate. I highly recommend this tape for singles.

Books Recommended

The Self Help Sourcebook: Finding and Forming Mutual Aid Self-Help Groups, 5th ed.

Self Help Clearinghouse, Denville, NJ 07834, 1995.

This is a comprehensive listing of support groups nation wide. It also includes a chapter on how to organize and run a self-help program.

Living Without Depression & Manic Depression
A Workbook for Maintaining Mood Stability

by Mary Ellen Copeland, M.S.

Publisher—New Harbinger, 1994

An excellent workbook for learning about mood disorders and maintaining stability using a whole person approach. I highly recommend this book.

The Depression Workbook
A Guide for Living with Depression

by Mary Ellen Copeland, M.S.

Publisher—New Harbinger, 1992

An excellent workbook for learning about mood disorders and maintaining stability using a multidimensional approach. I highly recommend this book.

Feeling Good—The New Mood Therapy

by David D. Burns

Publisher—Morrow

This book explains one of the proven methods for controlling mood swings—the cognitive (thought) approach. We can change our feelings and moods by changing the thoughts we think. Our thoughts can evoke and perpetuate our moods. It also contains a well balanced discussion of using medication vs. going to therapy (or doing both). Highly recommended.

Codependent No More

by Melody Beattie

Publisher—Harper/Hazelden

Explains what codependency is and how to deal with it. This book comes from the point of being codependent with an alcoholic. It is however, an excellent, informative book on understanding codependence in general, as well as alcoholic codependence.

191

Facing Codependence
> by Pia Mellody and Andrea Wells Miller
> Publisher—Harper Collins
>> This book treats codependence in a much more global fashion, not necessarily connecting it with alcoholic codependence. Pia and Andrea also have a workbook that can be used with this book to work through codependence. This workbook is called "Breaking Free."

Breaking Free
> By Pia Mellody and Andrea Wells Miller
> Publisher—Harper Collins
>> This is the workbook that goes with "Facing Codependence." It helps one to dig and find out what happened during childhood to cause such pain today. If we understand what happened to us and grieve our losses, we can heal and are less likely to pass our dysfunctional behavior down to our children. An excellent book.

The Road Less Traveled
> by M. Scott Peck, MD.
> Publisher—Touchstone
>> This is an excellent book in general. It is a fine book to learn about love, spirituality, mental illness, and growth. Get a look into the mind of a great psychiatrist and how he lovingly assists his clients on their journey to healing and wholeness.

Bradshaw On: The Family
> by John Bradshaw
> Publisher—Health Communications
>> This book is described in the video section of this Appendix.

As a Man Thinketh
> by James Allen
> Publisher—Grosset & Dunlap
>> An excellent and very short book of 72 pages. James Allen basically says that **we are what we think**. He explains very clearly why this is so. An empowering book.

Self Esteem

by McKay & Fanning

Publisher—Harbinger Publications

To summarize this book and how powerful it is, I would like to quote an excellent psychiatrist I once saw. When I showed it to her, she said, "That book is 20 years of my life; it took me 20 years to learn what that book contains." It is a very clear approach to improving one's self-esteem using cognitive techniques. Remember that low self-esteem is most often the root of depression and bipolar depression. This is a very readable book (easy to understand). It was written for the lay person.

Boundaries

When to Say Yes

When to Say No

To take control of your life

by Dr. Henry Cloud and Dr. John Townsend

Publisher—Zondervan Publishing House, 1992

I highly recommend this book to people who suffer from depression and bipolar. We usually have not been taught healthy boundaries in our childhood. Healthy boundary setting is part of being a healthy person. It is a big part of my recovery.

The Relaxation Response

by Herbert Benson, MD.

Publisher—Avon Books

This excellent book talks about the answer to modern-day stress which is "the relaxation response." It is a simple technique that Benson describes very clearly. He explains how to do it and why it works.

The Relaxation and Stress Reduction Workbook

by Davis, Ph.D., Eshelman, M.S.W. and McKay, Ph.D.

This book is filled with many different techniques to reduce stress. Since high levels of stress can   trigger episodes of depression and bipolar, this book is highly recommended to get well and to stay well.

193

Feel The Fear and Do It Anyway
> by Susan Jeffers Ph.D.
> Publisher—Ballantine Books 1987
>> Depression and manic depression are often triggered by fear and are highly fear-based and fear-sustained. This is an excellent book that shows how to work through fear which will help to heal depressive and manic depressive mood swings.

The Low Blood Sugar Handbook ISBN 0-916503-04-6
> by Edward and Patricia Krimmel, (c) 1992
> Publisher—Franklin Publishers
>> This book very clearly and concisely explains how low blood sugar can affect a person's bodily and mental functions. Low blood sugar can directly cause or add to the causes of depression and bipolar depression. They also give a large list of foods to eat and to avoid.

Love Gone Wrong
What to Do When You Are Attracted to the Wrong Person Over and Over
> by Thomas A. Whiteman, Ph.D and Randy Petersen
> Publisher—Nelson, 1994
>> If your depression or MD is triggered by relationship problems, this book is a must read. I have gone through incredible pain holding on too long in relationships. A test is included to tell if you are prone to relationship addiction.

STOP OBSESSING
How to Overcome Your Obsessions and Compulsions
> by Edna Foa, Ph.D. and Reid Wilson, Ph.D.
> Publisher—Bantam/Doubleday
>> Thinking in obsessive ways can lead to, as well as perpetuate, both depression and manic depression. Being able to recognize and stop obsessive thinking is crucial to healing depression and manic depression. This is a fine book that helps one to stop obsessive thinking.

Craving For Ecstasy (The Consciousness & Chemistry of Escape)
> by Harvey Milkman and Stanley Sunderwirth
> Publisher—Lexington Books, 1987
>> We can get high or low by the activities we engage in as well as through thinking in unhealthy ways. We can affect our brain chemistry without ever taking a drug. This book

194

tells how we do that, and how doing that often precedes the taking of external drugs which can lead to drug addiction.

Make Anger Your Ally
> by Dr. Neil Clark Warren, PH.D.
> Tyndale House Publishers, 1990
>> An excellent resource. Anger is most often involved in Depression & Bipolar Depression. If we want to heal we must find healthy and constructive ways to express our anger. Dr. Neil Clark Warren invites us to see the immense power of anger. He also shares wonderful possibilities for the constructive use of anger when we make anger our ally.

Depression and the Body
> by Alexander Lowen
> Publisher—Pelican
>> The title describes this book. A useful and non classical approach toward dealing with depression

Growing Up on Television
> by Kate Moody
> Publisher—Times Books, 1980
>> Kate Moody very clearly explains the effect television is having on children and shaping our society, including: physical, learning and perception, reading, promoting aggressive behavior, health, social relationships, and more.

What to Say When You Talk to Yourself
> by Shad Helmstetter
> Publisher—Pocket Books
>> I once heard Helmstetter on a talk show. He described beautifully how our bodies and brains can get into a state of chemical imbalance. There is a switch in our brain that when flipped can cause toxins to be dumped into our systems, causing a chemical imbalance. This switch is called "a thought." He explains how to bring our systems back into balance by wholesome thought and self-affirmations.

The Secret of Staying in Love
>   by John Powell
>   Publisher—Argus Communications
>>   This book is about communication—how important it is, and how to communicate well. It is about love and how essential love is. It speaks about what love is, what love is not, and how to love well. It also speaks about how the lack of proper love can lead to mental and physical illness, and how the presence of real love can heal us.

What Color Is Your Parachute?
>   by Bolles
>   Publisher—Ten Speed Press, 1994
>>   This is an excellent book to help learn how to search for a job. It is also excellent in helping one to determine if a career change is needed. It then helps the reader determine which particular career might be the most suitable for them.

Finding Balance
>   (12 priorities for interdependence and joyful living)
>   by Terry Kellog and Marvel Harrison
>   Publisher—Health Communications Inc.
>>   Sometimes we get so recovery-oriented and problem-focused that we lose balance in our lives. This book integrates joy, fun, play and the concept of interdependence into the recovery process.

The Hug Therapy Book
>   by Keating
>   Publisher—Compcar
>>   This is a short and cute, but very powerful description of how important hugs are. It includes excellent and humorous illustrations.

Pulling Your Own Strings
>   by Dr. Wayne W. Dyer
>   Publisher—Avon
>>   Dr. Dyer tells us specific ways people try to pull our strings and control us. He informs the reader of the warning signs of this and also gives ways to counter the manipulative attempts that people make to try and control us.

Psychosomatics
>> By Howard R. and Martha E. Lewis
>> Publisher—Pinnacle Books
>>> This book is filled with information on how our emotions affect our health. It relates specific illnesses to certain personality types.

Moodswing (The Third Revolution in Psychiatry)
>> by Dr. Ronald R. Fieve, MD.
>> Publisher—Bantam Books
>>> For anyone interested in the chemical approach to coping with manic depression, this book is a good source. It also has other interesting information including some case histories. It seems that Fieve thinks lithium is the answer.

Toxic Psychiatry: Why Therapy, Empathy, and Love Must Replace the Drugs, Electroshock, and Biochemical Theories of the New Psychiatry
>> by Peter R. Breggin, 1994
>>> If you want to feel that your depression or bipolar symptoms are normal given your situation and upbringing; If you want to read an eye-opening discourse on the flaws with the *bio-chemical imbalance* theories—read this book!

Your Drug May Be Your Problem:
How and Why to Stop Taking Psychiatric Medications
>> by Peter R., Md Breggin, David, Phd Cohen, 2000
>>> This book is certainly a good balance for the culture we live in that seems to take drugs at the drop of a hat. The authors, a psychiatrist and a Ph. D. offer some compelling reasons why we should not take psychotropic medications. They also give clear advice on how to stop taking medicines in as safe a way as possible. They may be a bit extreme in terms of not taking meds at all, but all of us should read their reasons! We can then decide for ourselves.

For anyone interested in the question, how do I love in a healthy way? The following books are excellent resources:

The Road Less Traveled
>> by M. Scott Peck
>>> For description see previous section.

Unconditional Love
>by John Powell
>
>Publisher—Argus Communications
>
>>This is a gift from John Powell about "Unconditional Love"—what it is and how to attain it. This book is only 118 pages (for those who like short, but good books).

The Secret of Staying in Love
>by John Powell
>
>>For description see previous section.

The Little Prince
>by Antoine De Saint Exupery
>
>Publisher—Harcourt, Brace & World, Inc.
>
>>A beautiful and favorite story of mine about love and life. Its symbolism is unique. The Little Prince challenges us as to what is really important in life. He also presents rituals that we so often forget as we relate to other people, especially in love. He is also refreshing in showing us how important it is to ask the right questions and to be persistent. He reminds us to laugh!

Love Is Letting Go of Fear
>by Gerald G. Jampolsky, MD.
>
>Publisher—Bantam Books
>
>>In this book Dr. Jampolsky brings to light how "fear" is at the root of almost all mental, physical, and relational problems. He talks about why this is so, and presents clear ways to overcome this block to love.

Loving Each Other
>by Leo Buscaglia, Ph.D.
>
>Publisher—Fawcett Communications
>
>>For people who are afraid that they might be crazy, Leo thinks it is good to be considered crazy. People who are considered crazy are allowed to be who they are! Love is crazy. Love is beautiful, and love is hugs, lots of them. If you like these thoughts, I think you'll like Leo's book.

Joshua

by Joseph Girzone

Publisher—Collier Books

If Jesus were to live again in the 1990's, what might he be like? How would He love? How might He respond to some present day things that divide us? How might He attempt to disassemble *the walls* that divide us and restore the two great commands: Love God with your whole heart, with your whole soul, with your whole mind, and with all of your strength; and: Love thy neighbor as thyself?

Gandhi the Man

by Eknath Easwaran

Publisher—Nilgiri Press

An excellent work on the life of Gandhi, a man who lived love. He was a man who had a true sense of humility, who knew that sometimes love is gentle and sometimes it must be tough (if it is real). Gandhi also knew and lived the price of love, which often involves suffering for the object of our love. Suffering hurts, but the rewards are awesome (if we suffer lovingly).

Peace Pilgrim Her Life and Work in Her Own Words

by Peace Pilgrim

Publisher—Ocean Tree Books

An incredible woman who made her life a prayer. Peace gave up all she owned except for the tunic she wore. She fasted until given food and walked until given shelter. Peace walked over 25,000 miles around the United States and Canada preaching the message of peace. Her motto "Overcome evil with good, falsehood with truth, and hatred with love." This book is available, free, just call 714–927–7678.

The Holy Bible

This is the Greatest Book of love, truth and healing that there is. My hope is that my book may serve as a pointer to the real truth, the real Healer, which is Jesus. He "lived love" to its fullest. Don't miss the healing and guidance found in the Bible.

APPENDIX C

WHAT IS CODEPENDENCE?

T here are several aspects to Codependence. It involves thinking styles and behaviors that were learned in our early childhood which worked for us then, but they do not work well for us in our adulthood. To the contrary, they often sabotage our adult relationships.

Several indications of codependence follow:

- A core symptom of codependence is poor self-esteem.
- Codependents are usually too dependent on external circumstances and the approval of others for their happiness and sense of worth.
- They are like puppets dangling from the strings of circumstance and *other*-approval.
- Another symptom of codependence is *living in the extremes*.

Doesn't that sound like bipolar behavior (living in the extremes)?
Isn't poor self-esteem directly related to depression?

These points are precisely why so much healing has come to me through Codependence Anonymous support groups. They never tried to medicate me. They never diagnosed me or labeled me. They never saw me as different—weird. Rather, my fellow members accept me as I am and understand me. We heal together as we share our stories and our hurts with the group. We work to correct the dysfunctional thinking and behaviors which we learned in our childhood.

201

Codependents are often trying to control the behavior of another person. They often have a problem controlling their own behavior. Hence, control of self and others are issues for the codependent.

A codependent may manipulate another to get what they want, instead of asking directly. Codependents most often have boundary problems. They don't know where they end and someone else begins. In relationships, they struggle with knowing what is their responsibility and what is not. They often say yes to people when they want to say no.

Codependents often look for others to make them happy. On the other side, they are prone to feel responsible for other peoples feelings. A parent of a codependent person often sets a person up for codependence by saying things such as this to their child, " Jimmy, you made mommy feel bad." Hearing statements like that, a child begins to feel responsible for the feelings of the parent. Such statements and mind-sets are very unhealthy and a heavy load for a child to bear.

A person who suffers from codependence might also be an enabler for a dependent person. Hence, the term—codependent. An example of this would be the wife of an alcoholic who calls into work for the alcoholic to say he is sick when he is really having a hangover. Another example might be: a sister who keeps bailing her brother out by giving him money after he spends his own irresponsibly and can't pay his rent. Without the codependent, the dependent person would not be able to continue his or her dependent and irresponsible behavior.

Some characteristics of families that codependents come from are: speaking one's mind is discouraged, sharing of one's feelings is discouraged and trust is not fostered. This is oppression. Human beings need to be free to speak their mind. We need to be allowed to feel, and express our feelings. We need to be able to trust.

Codependents may also control others and get what they want by being outwardly demanding and overpowering. They may yell and rage to get what they want. Manipulation is covertly (secretly) forceful. Demanding and overpowering is being overtly (openly) forceful. Both are codependent and unhealthy ways to get what we want.

Codependent thinking and behaviors thwart intimacy and love. They work against them.

To heal from codependence, we must accept responsibility for our own thoughts and feelings. We must learn to get our needs met in healthy ways. We must reclaim our power. We must gain self-control and let go of other-control.

What else could you do if you think you might have a problem with codependence? Learn more about it. There are several excellent books listed in Appendix B that describe codependence in detail as well as how to heal from it. I would also highly suggest getting into a CODA 12-step support group. Healing comes socially, not just from reading books. To find the nearest CODA meeting, look in Appendix A for the phone number of CODA National. They can direct you to a group in your area. The psychology department at a local college or university might also know of a group nearby. Many churches donate their space to 12-step groups. They often have lists too. If you cannot find a CODA group nearby, try an ACOA (Adult Children of Alcoholics) group. Many of the issues are similar and there are many ACOA groups.

If you are not yet ready for a group environment, then you may want to find a therapist who understands codependence. Hopefully the therapist you choose is in, or has been in, CODA themselves.

Remember, one can get codependent with a therapist or even with CODA too. Use your judgment. Keep your head in whatever healing environment you choose. Don't sell your soul, your heart or your mind to anyone. Do not become too dependent on any one person or group. Nor let any one person or group become too dependent on you. Our total dependence must be on God alone.

QUALITIES TO SEEK IN A PARTNER

and

in Friendships

B elow is a list of values and qualities a person suffering from depression or bipolar depression should look for in a potential life partner (and even in friendships). I believe anyone who suffers from mood swings would benefit from seeking a person with these qualities.

- Someone who doesn't believe in labels.
- Someone who believes in *growth*.
- Someone who accepts them for who they are today, regardless of their past. This attitude, as well as the entire section here should go both ways in the relationship.
- Someone who will not let the fears of other people become their fears.
- Someone who will accept them and love them despite their behaviors.
- They need someone who will accept and love them whether they are healthy or even if and "especially if" they ever suffer from a relapse of bipolar type of behavior again.
- In short, they need a mature partner.
- A person who is unafraid, or at least who plows through their fears with courage and faith.
- They need a partner who is *consistent* and not questioning whether they want to leave the relationship after every little conflict. They need someone who is sure and committed, not someone who needs everything to be "right" for them to stay, not someone who thinks a relationship

should "just work," but someone who is willing to make the relationship work.

- They need a partner who believes in them and encourages them.
- The partner must believe in himself or herself as well.
- For myself, I needed someone who loved God and was Christian—as I myself was. I wanted someone who was not just talking the talk, but someone who was walking the walk.
- It is also a great advantage to have a partner who knows herself or himself and has done some of her or his own healing work, not someone who believes that you have a problem and she or he doesn't.
- It is also helpful if their partner believes in similar healing methods that they believe in.
- Someone who is honest and trustworthy.
- Someone who has good communication skills.
- Someone who can handle conflict and anger and has skills, love, and the will to work though these.
- Someone who likes to play and have fun and has a good sense of humor.
- Someone they have a lot in common with.
- Someone who likes to eat healthy mood stabilizing foods.
- Someone who is emotionally mature.
- Someone who is humble, but not a pushover.
- Someone who is dependable.
- A person who is patient and kind.

On the following page are qualities that are usually *not* wise to have in a friend or especially a mate.

Qualities that are usually **not good** in friends or a mate

- People who can't commit.
- People who won't look at themselves and own their problems.
- People who can't handle occasional anger or upset.
- People who are angry all of the time.
- People who are manipulative.
- People who are perfectionists and who think they are perfect.
- People who are worriers.
- People who are critical much (or all) of the time.
- People who don't have good boundaries.
- People who don't share—they hold all of their feelings and emotions in.
- People who don't respect you and what you treasure.
- People who are into excessive drinking or drugs.
- People who send mixed messages (for example: their mouth says I love you but their actions are to the contrary).
- People who are unappreciative.
- People who discount your good deeds and accomplishments.
- People who say you are too sensitive.
- People who engage in destructive (or hurtful) humor or teasing.
- People who can't forgive.
- People who aren't humble enough to admit when they are wrong.
- People who can't say, "I'm sorry."
- People who are always blaming others for their problems.
- People who are very controlling.
- Someone who is very moody.
- People who discount or invalidate your feelings.

CHARTS

<u>Feel free to copy, carry, and use any of the following charts.</u>

Feelings Chart

Feeling (joy, peace, happy, relaxed, fearful, lonely, sad, tense, depressed or high)	Date and Time	Thought/Event which preceded feeling	Action taken and resulting feeling

I find this chart works very well for me. When I have a strong feeling, I write it down and immediately correct my thoughts if they are painful. If they are good, I enjoy them and note the thoughts or action that caused them. I learn to maximize joyful and peaceful feelings. I keep a copy of this chart folded in my pocket.

Annual Highs And Lows Chart

General Mood for Month	Month	Events Happening Relational problems, stress-(pos. or neg.), holidays, tragedies, happy events or internal struggles. Days getting shorter/longer.
	Jan.	
	Feb.	
	Mar.	
	Apr.	
	May	
	June	
	July	
	Aug.	
	Sept.	
	Oct.	
	Nov.	
	Dec.	

Note: This chart will help understand what's happening and when. It will also help predict which might be bad months or good months in general. Hence, one might prepare extra rest time in normally tough months. It should be filled out for the past several years and also on an ongoing basis.

Daily Highs And Lows Chart

General Mood of the Day	Day and Date	Events Happening Relational Prob., Days shorter/longer, Stresses (pos. or neg.) Holidays, tragedies, happy events or internal struggles.
	Sun.	
	Mon.	
	Tues.	
	Wed.	
	Thur.	
	Fri.	
	Sat.	

Note: This chart will help understand what's happening and when on a daily basis. It will also help predict which might be bad days or good days in general. Hence, one might prepare extra rest time on normally tough days of the week. It should be filled out for the past several weeks and also on an ongoing basis. It may also be helpful to rate the day from 1-10 (10 being best). That'll be easy to graph.

Appendix F

WEB SITES

Helpful Internet Resources (to get you started)

You'll find some more hopeful and helpful information at the following site. The author's current *seminar* information will be included. This book and others may be ordered at this site (often at a discounted rate). **The author's email address may be found here.** Feedback concerning this book is welcome. Suggestions for inclusion in future books is welcomed. *Personal stories of healing are welcome.* You'll find links to some helpful sites in addition to the ones below:
www.manicdepression.org

Self-Help Resources on the Internet:
http://www.psych-web.com/resource/selfhelp.htm

Depressionweb.com - DEPRESSION & Suicide Prevention
(Hot Lines!!! Listed by State and local area)
(Depression, Suicide, just talk, etc)
http://www.depressionweb.com/

Suicide Crisis Center SUICIDE HOTLINES:
http://suicidal.com/suicideprevention/hotlines.html

Mary Ellen Copeland's WEB site:
Highest recommendation! Mary Ellen has struggled with difficult depressions and manic depressions. She is now in solid recovery. Mary Ellen is a counselor, teacher, speaker, and has written several *excellent* books on overcoming depression and manic depression using a truly whole person approach (many methods). Visit her site to get loads of good information:
www.mentalhealthrecovery.com

National Empowerment Center (NEC)
Highly recommended! This organization promotes self empowerment and gives many success stories about people who have recovered from mental illness. They put out a great news letter. It is run by people who have had emotional illnesses and have recovered:
www.power2u.org

Resource on Cognitive Therapy:
Contains links to find cognitive therapists around the country!
www.FeelingGood.com

John Bradshaw's Web Site:
Contains most of Bradshaw's Video's and books. I highly recommend these resources—especially his Video titled: *Bradshaw: On The Family*
http://www.bradshawcassettes.com/

Depression Bookstore
http://suicidal.com/depressionbookstore/categories/manicdepression/

Psychiatrist—Dr. Peter Breggin's web site:
You must visit this web site—especially if you want information concerning psychiatric medications and if you should take them or not. Breggin gives eye-opening information why maybe you should not take them. He also lists wholesome treatment centers
www.breggin.com

Worlds largest online bookstore & music store:
www.amazon.com

NEW BOOK section - depression books etc.
http://suicidal.com/depressionbookstore/newbooks/

Dr. Ivan's Depression Central (lots of good stuff and www sites):
http://www.psycom.net/depression.central.html

Medications for Bipolar Disorder
people have the right to decide:
http://www.pendulum.org/meds.htm

Medications ***nice*** DMD meds used and side-effects:
http://www.mentalhealth.com/p30.html

FUN!!:
http://www.sunmoments.com/inspire.html

Manic Depression FUN Page: (Some humor is good. Some is off color.)
http://www.tigger1.demon.co.uk/depression/index.html

DSM-IV Classification: (Official Book of Psychological Diagnosis)
http://wwwsb.ccsu.ctstateu.edu/Faculty/frost/415/DSMClassifications.html

Drugs and Medications:
http://www.yahoo.com/Health/Pharmacy/Drugs_and_Medications/Specific_
Drugs_and_Medications/ *(note: these 2 lines are really 1 continuous line)*

Focus On The Family:
www.family.org

Christain radio-Family Life Today:
www.fltoday.org

Taizé music and the Taizé letter can be found at:
http://www.taize.fr

Mental Health Net:
Job resource for people who suffer from emotional/psychological problems
http://www.cmhc.com/joblink/

Another fine resource is New Life Ministries:
http://www.newlife.com/

For Dr. Henry Cloud's book *Boundaries* and other great resources visit:
www.CloudTownsend.com

Please Note:

Web sites come and go and are changing all of the time. Some of these may change or possibly be unavailable by the time you read this book. Most will remain and they'll get you started. From those that work, you will be able to find links to other sites. Use discretion when obtaining information from web sites. Don't believe everything you hear or read. Use discernment.

INDEX

Depression (cont.)
and hormones, 46
mild, 27, 32
and oppression, 55
as reaction to loss, 53
and stress, 149
and sugar, 147-48
symptoms of, 29-32
and therapy, 76-79, 106-8, 143
tools for handling, 71-120
as a whirlpool, 129
Depressive/Manic Depressive Support
Group (DMDSG), 67-68, 153, 171-72
Deprivation:
love, 47-49
sleep, 29, 34, 36
Destructive tapes, rewriting, 72-73
Dietary comparison, 155
Diet/nutrition, 69, 88-89, 123-24,
147-58, 177
low blood sugar symptoms, 147-48
and recovery, 152-53
sugar, 147-48
Distractions, 104
and high side of bipolar disorder, 118
Diversity, and high side of bipolar, 114
Divorce, as societal pressure, 52
Drinking fluids, 105
"Dripping" of stress/pressures, 40
Drugs, and depression, 46-47
Drug trap, 66-67

E
Eliminating unnecessary tasks,
100
Emotional discipline, 114
Emotional immaturity, 41
Emotional integration, 107-8
as societal pressure, 51
Emotional needs, 121, 126
Emotional numbness, as sign of
depression, 30
Encouragement:
and depression, 139
and high side of bipolar disorder, 146
Environment:
corrosive, 71-72
as societal pressure, 62-63

Euphoria, 33, 73
and bowel disturbance, 34
depression vs., 73
See also
Tools for handling the high side,
High side of bipolar disorder
Exaggerated thoughts, as sign of
depression, 31
Exercise, 69, 83, 87, 124
of free will, 102
and high side of bipolar disorder, 114
scheduling of physical exercise, 131
Expectations, lowering, 101
Expression of emotions/feelings,
learning in support groups, 68
External environment, 62-63
Extremes, and mania, 35-36

F
Facing Codependence (Melody), 110
Failure, handling, 101
Faith:
daily devotional, 161
and healing, 160-61
power of, 159-68
prayer, 162-63
thoughts on, 163-64
Family, 103-4
Family counseling, 76-77
Family system, 172
Family system problems, 21
Family systems theory, 69, 76
Fear:
of punishment, 17
as societal pressure, 53-54
Feelings, 94
charting, 110
expressing, 130
Feelings Chart, 213
Feeling your feelings, 171
and high side of bipolar disorder,
116
Fight or flight response, 149
Flour, refined, 149
Fluids, 151-52, drinking, 105
Focus:
and depression, 82
and high side of bipolar disorder, 114

221

Following your dream, 91
Food, *See* Diet/nutrition
Forgiveness, 80, 99, 107, 130
  lack of, 41
Free will, exercising, 102
Friendships:
  developing, 100-101
  and high side of bipolar disorder, 117
Fruits, 151

G
Gandhi, Mahatma, 96-97
Genes, 61-62
Genetic approach, 69
Giving burnout, 43
Glucose, 149
Glucose tolerance test (GTT), 156
Grandiose thoughts, and mania, 34, 35
Guilt, 44
  and depression, 17
  giving out of, 141

H
Habits, 112
Hard physical work, 83
Harmony, 122
Hate, turning into a prayer, 80-81
Healing, 161
  whole-person, 65, 69
Health, of caregiver, 139-41, 145-46
Healthy people, spending time with, 87
Healthy thoughts, 80-81
Helmstetter, Shad, 66
Healthy ways of relating,
  and support groups, 68
High side of bipolar disorder:
  and acceptance, 145
  and anger, 33, 35, 94, 116, 119, 174
  and caregiver's love, 146
  compared to low side, 35-36
  and critical thinking, 115-16
  and distractions, 118
  and diversity, 114
  early warning signs of, 134
  and encouragement, 146
  and exercise, 114
  and feeling your feelings, 116

  and focus, 114
  and friendships, 117
  helping someone through, 143-46
  and hot baths, 117
  judgment, 144-45
  and massage, 118-19
  and medication, 119
  and meditation, 146
  and music, 118
  and naps, 117
  and nature, 118
  and negative thinking, 115-16
  and peer counseling, 117-18
  and rest, 116
  and sleep, 115
  and suicidal thoughts, 35
  and support groups, 115
  and therapy, 113, 146
  tools for handling, 113-20
  and touching, 118-19
  and trigger people, 118
  and validation, 145
  and water, 116
Hobbies, 87
Hope, 15-26, 90, 143
Hopefulness, 34
Hopelessness, as sign of depression, 29
Hormones, and depression, 46
Hot baths, and high side of bipolar disorder, 117
Hugs, 106, 142
Human needs, 121-67
  balancing, 130-33
  body, 121, 122-25
  emotional, 121, 126
  mind, 121, 125
  social, 121, 126-27
  spirit, 121, 125-26
Humility, and healing process, 79
Hygiene changes, as sign of depression, 31
Hypoglycemia, 153-54

I
Ignoring, as unhealthy communication method, 50
Imagination, 92

222

Protein, 88, 151
Prozac, 19, 149, 150
Psychoanalytical approach, 69
Psychosomatic approach, 69
Psychosomatics, 17
    behavioral symptoms, 18
    and guilt, 17
    and love, 18
Punishment, fear of, 17
Purpose, 131
Put-downs, as unhealthy communication
    method, 50

Q
Quiet time, 85-86

R
Reading, 125
Recalling past accomplishments, 90
Recovery:
    author's personal experience of, 169-86
    Codependents Anonymous (CODA),
    172
    Depressive/Manic Depressive Support
        Group (DMDSG), 171-72
    family system, 172
    feeling feelings, 171
    inner child work, 172
    major events, 169-70
    meditative prayer, 171
    staying connected, 172
    will training, 171
Redirecting thoughts, 131
Refined carbohydrates, 149
Refined flour, 149
Refined sugar, 131
Relationship addiction:
    and depression, 47-49
Relaxation tape, 120
Rest, 124-25, 131
    and high side of bipolar disorder, 116
Road Less Traveled, The (Peck), 63

S
St. John's Wort, 157
Sarcasm, as unhealthy communication
    method, 50
Schedules, 106

Scheduling, and structure, 109
Seasonal Affective Disorder (SAD), 55
Secret of Staying in Love, The (Powell),
    63, 142
Selective serotonin-reuptake inhibitors
    (SSRIs), 149
Self-awareness, and support groups, 68
Self-control imbalance, 33-34, 35
Self-destructiveness: as sign of
    depression, 30
Self-empowerment, 101
Self-esteem, 36, 50, 77, 100
    high, 33
Self-expression, release of, 34
Self-help phone numbers, 187-88
Self-Help resource book, 75
Self-indulgence, 33
Self-knowledge, 92
Self-pressures, 41-49
    anger, 43
    catastrophic thinking, 42
    child abuse, 45-46
    commitment, 44
    control, 44
    drugs, 46-47
    emotional immaturity, 41
    giving burnout, 43
    guilt, 44
    imbalance, 42
    inaction, 43
    isolation, 47
    lack of forgiveness, 41
    negative/critical thinking, 41
    polarized thinking, 41-42
    pride, 47
    relationship addiction, 47-49
    stress, 42-43
    unrealistic dreams, 44
Self-suppression:
    as sign of depression, 31
Seminar information, 229
Serotonin, 93
    selective serotonin-reuptake
        inhibitors (SSRIs), 149
    and stress, 150
Sex, lack of interest in, as sign of
    depression, 30
Sexual appetite, increasing, 34

225

227

To order, write a note or copy & send order form with payment

Overcoming Depression and Manic Depression (Bipolar Disorder) A Whole-Person Approach answers the questions: What do I do other than taking medication to get well and stay well? What can care givers do to help? One reader wrote: "No book comes at healing from so many angles as this one."

This book may be ordered at any Barnes & Noble,
Borders, or any other bookstore that has "Books in Print."
This book may be purchased online from:

www.manicdepression.org
(Books are often discounted here.)
Author's current seminar schedule and email address may be found here.

www.amazon.com

www.barnesandnoble.com

*Paul Wider is available for Seminars
at your location.
Call **Wellness Communications** at:
201-804-7735
or write to the above address.*

Order Form

Send $18.95 per copy, and $3 for postage & handling = $21.95 (For priority mail add $2 shipping).
Send check or money order to: **Wellness Communications, 120 Morse Ave, Rutherford, NJ 07070**
Orders outside USA must pay in US dollars using a money order.   NJ residents include sales tax.

Send To: Please Print or type

Mr./Ms. _____

Address _____

City _____ State _____ Zip _____

Phone number -include area code (____) -_____

Email Address: _____

Price subject to change without notice

229